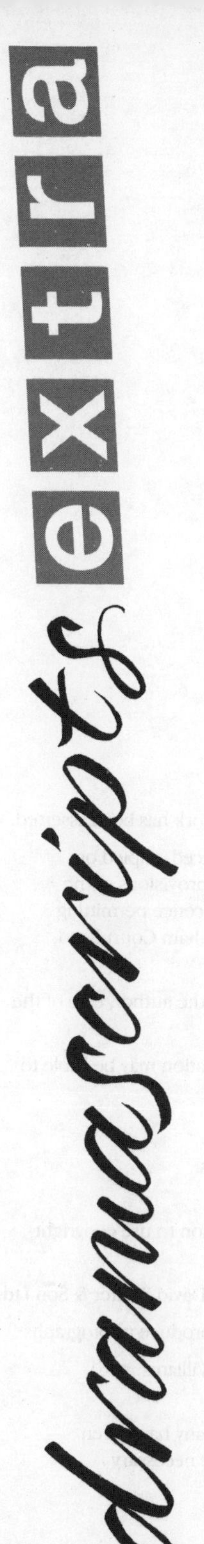

THE LAST LAUGH

Series Editor: *Andy Kempe*

The original Dramascripts series was created and edited by Guy Williams.

Nelson

Thomas Nelson and Sons Ltd
Nelson House Mayfield Road
Walton-on-Thames Surrey
KT12 5PL UK

51 York Place
Edinburgh
EH1 3JD UK

Thomas Nelson (Hong Kong) Ltd
Toppan Building 10/F
22a Westlands Road
Quarry Bay Hong Kong

Thomas Nelson Australia
102 Dodds Street
South Melbourne
Victoria 3205 Australia

Nelson Canada
1120 Birchmount Road
Scarborough Ontario
M1K 5G4 Canada

First published by Thomas Nelson and Sons Ltd 1993

ISBN 0-17-432489-8
NPN 9 8 7 6 5 4 3 2 1

Printed in Hong Kong.

Acknowledgement is due to John Aldridge for advising on this series.

ACKNOWLEDGEMENTS
The authors and publishers wish to thank the following for permission to use copyright material:

The Attempted Assassination of the Queen by William McGonagall. David Winter & Son Ltd.

Acknowledgement is also due to the following for permission to reproduce photographs:

The BBC: p. 62; Hulton Picture Company: p. 7, 65(2); Punch/Mike Williams: p. 61; Retna: p. 65; Syndication International p. 65.

Every effort has been made to trace all the copyright holders, but if any have been inadvertently overlooked the publishers will be pleased to make the necessary arrangements at the first opportunity.

CONTENTS

INTRODUCTION iv

FOREWORD vi

CAST LIST viii

THE PLAY: THE LAST LAUGH 1

ACTIVITIES 51

FIRST RESPONSES 52

Talking Points 52
Write 54
Verse and Worse 55
Drama 57

PLAYING THE CHARACTERS 58

A Fairy Tale? 58
Funnier than Fiction 60
Doctor Bleach 63
Bobby Bunting 63

DRAWING ATTENTION 66

Amnesty International 66
The Pen is Mightier Than the Sword 68
Pictures with a Purpose 70

INTRODUCTION

DRAMASCRIPTS EXTRA

Dramascripts Extra is a series of plays which can be explored in the classroom, the drama studio or on the stage. Most of the plays in the series were written for performance by professional theatre companies. They are included because their language and structure is accessible to pupils studying English and Drama and because they are concerned with issues relevant to a young audience.

The playscripts are presented in a readable and attractive way without affecting the different styles and demands of the playwrights.

Each play is accompanied by an Activities section which offers teachers and pupils ideas for work which focuses on the play as a written text, the way it might be produced on stage and the themes and issues it explores. The activities cover the Attainment Targets for English at KS 3 and 4 through a range of carefully focused individual and group orientated tasks. Many of the tasks are practical, but while a large room or studio would be an ideal, teachers should find that clearing the desks to one side will give them enough space to tackle most of these exercises.

Andy Kempe, the series editor, taught drama in comprehensive schools for ten years. He is an established author in this field and now lectures in Drama in Education at the University of Reading.

THE LAST LAUGH

The Last Laugh was first produced in 1984. Since then the world has changed a great deal. Certainly, it is hard to believe that anyone could have predicted what happened to the political face of Eastern Europe at the end of the 1980s.

On 21 December 1989 news screens were dominated by the picture of the Romanian President Ceausescu looking bewildered as the crowds in the square below started to whistle and jeer at him. The unthinkable was happening; people who had lived in fear of his regime for twenty-five years were literally singing out their derision. Ceausescu's face didn't so much depict anger as a complete incomprehension as to what was happening. His inability to understand the situation arose from his inability to understand that people have certain rights which, though they can be violated, can never be totally dispensed with.

The Last Laugh isn't about the fall of Ceausescu though some of the scenes in it do uncannily reflect the events of December 1989. Nor is it specifically about any of the many other countries which oppress individuals or whole sections of the population by the denial of human rights. It certainly isn't a play that takes a smug attitude about how good life is in 'the free world' either. Ben Payne refers to his play as a 'fairy tale'. Fairy tales can give insights into the societies which cherish them and pass them down through generations. But they can also be deliberately manufactured and passed off as 'reality'. When this happens, 'fairy tales' become pernicious strategies of oppression.

FOREWORD

I first wrote this play when I was 17. I read somewhere about a 14 year old Argentinian boy called Juan Nughes. One day, armed police walked into his school, took him away and he was never seen again.

It was the last phrase of his story: 'and he was never seen again' that stuck with me. It reminded me of the ending of a fairy tale. But unlike fairy tales, Juan's story, like the stories of many other young people all over the world who had 'disappeared', was true. I could have written about any one of those specific cases. Instead, I wrote a fairy tale; a fantasy about a country whose government has outlawed laughter. It didn't have to be laughter of course. It could just as well have been a law against eating chocolate or wearing striped pyjamas if the consequences of breaking that law were the same. But I decided that laughter would be the worst crime in this country because it would mean that whoever laughed saw the strangeness of their situation and found it ridiculous.

The world has changed quickly since I first wrote this play. Sometimes it seems as if we watch these changes like an audience in a play. We are detached, superior. But this is the biggest fantasy of all, for we must keep asking whether our own 'free' way of seeing the world isn't also shaped by our own fairy tales masquerading as reality. Who decides whose stories are heard and whose stories are not? We know that Juan was never seen again, but why not? Perhaps simply because he – or someone close to him – asked the same question of a government that would not tolerate being questioned.

The Last Laugh is dedicated to Amnesty International because for over thirty years it has defended the right to ask questions.

Ben Payne

Zar Gana has been described as the most famous stand-up comedian in Burma. In 1988, the Burmese people protested against 26 years of harsh military rule, and Zar Gana performed at the mass rallies that called for a return of free elections.

He was arrested for satirising the President, General Saw Maung, and is presently believed to be serving a 5 year prison sentence in Insien Prison.

Zar Gana is just one of the many prisoners of conscience Amnesty International has campaigned for since its formation in 1961.

Piers Bannister
Amnesty International

CAST LIST

Soldier One
a soldier

Soldier Two
another soldier

Bobby Bunting
a travelling salesman

Gilbert Grimm
a world leader

Gloria Grimm
another world leader

Grizzelda Grimm
their daughter

Mr Left
a bodyguard

Mr Right
another bodyguard

Mrs Dismal
an ordinary woman

Mrs Dull
another ordinary woman

Prisoners
in the Prison for Chronic Comedians

Dr Bleach
a doctor

The Last Laugh was first performed by students from the Havant Sixth Form College in 1984. A revised version was produced at the Edinburgh Festival in 1991. It was directed by Patrick Wilde.

THE LAST LAUGH

1 THE CELL

The glare from a single bulb lights the first page of a large open book. A voice is heard.

The Book This book has lain here long in jail
Since its pages told an untrue tale
Of a land, once upon a time,
Where laughter once was made a crime.
Its sad, cold folk lived deep in fear
Beyond its grey and grim frontier.
A line dividing right from wrong
Two guards had guarded hard and long.
Dogged lads, obeying orders
Getting boreder, boreder on the border

The page magically turns.

An empty horizon. A dotted line crosses the stage left to right.

***Soldier 1** and **Soldier 2** stand on guard. Beside them an old weatherworn sign which says YOU ARE NOW ENTERING A FUN-FREE COUNTRY. NO LAUGHING FROM THIS POINT ON.*

They march up and down the dotted line once, then stop, then face out.

Pause

Soldier 1 So Soldier Two – here we are. Here we are, week after week, day after day, hour after hour – guarding the border of our country …

Soldier 2 … border …

Soldier 1 And you know, Soldier Two, while we've been looking at this empty horizon I've been wondering. If there was a special award for doing the most boring job in the world would we get it? I mean, could we be any more bored than this?

Soldier 2 … border …

Soldier 1 Ah. So we're not of the same mind then, us two, Soldier Two. Because this is the most boring job I've ever done. And, let me tell you, I've done some incredibly boring jobs in my time. *(Pause)* Have I ever told you before about the incredibly boring jobs I've done in my time, Soldier Two?

***Soldier 2** nods twice, slowly, sadly.*

I once guarded the State Graveyard for Not Very Important Dead People. Tremendously boring that was. Didn't think there was a job that could get me …

Soldier 2 … border …

Soldier 1 … than that. Oh, but I was wrong. I was so good at guarding, our glorious leaders Gilbert and Gloria Grimm posted me here. And from then on I got …

Soldier 2 … border …

Soldier 1 … and …

Soldier 2 … border …

Soldier 1 … until now all I can talk about is how much …

Soldier 2 … border …

Soldier 1 … I am than the last time I talked about it. So, of anyone, from one farthest-flung border to the other farthest-flung border of this glorious country which is so gloriously boring no one would ever think of coming here, I think we deserve that special award for doing the job that's the last word, the ultimate, the number one in all-time, big-time tedium: guarding the …

Both … border.

Pause. Soldier 2 blinks.

Soldier 2 What is the point, Soldier One?

Soldier 1 Of what, Soldier Two?

Soldier 2 What is the point of guarding the border of a country where no one would ever think of coming?

Pause

Soldier 1 The point is – they *might.* At any moment the enemy, them, over there, the Cheerful People might suddenly swarm across this border to cheer us up.

Soldier 2 comes to attention and points his rifle out.

Soldier 2 *(grimly)* Just let them try it, Soldier One.

Soldier 1 That's the spirit, Soldier Two. Always steady, always ready, … if those Cheerful People should ever suddenly swarm across this border … here we are … always on guard, hour after hour, week after week … month after …

***Bunting** enters suddenly. The **Soldiers** jump. He is carrying a travelling salesman's case.*

Bunting ***(cheerfully)*** Good morning, friends.

Soldier 2 What is it, Soldier One?

***Bunting** extends his hand and grins.*

It's showing its teeth. Is it angry about something?

Soldier 1 ***(pushing Soldier 2)*** Ask it what it wants, Soldier Two?

Soldier 2 What do you want?

Bunting I'd like free passage to cross this border on purposes of business, please.

Soldier 2 What sort of business?

Bunting A very good question and wouldn't you like to know? I bet you would. I bet you're just itching to find out what I've got in this very ordinary-looking but really very extraordinary suitcase, aren't you? Well, in here just happens to be one of the most brilliant inventions of the human race.

Soldier 1 What's that then?

Bunting Guess.

Soldier 1 ***(thinks. He can't guess.)*** Search that suitcase, Soldier Two. ***(Soldier 2 snatches the case)***

Bunting Go ahead, feel free, take a look – what is in that suitcase is – a sense of humour! Yes, that's right, a sense of humour: that rare and precious quality understood and loved the world over. Allow me to introduce myself: Bobby Bunting, salesman of top quality jokes and novelties, each and every one a guaranteed scream ***(Soldier 2 encounters something in the case which makes him yelp)*** There you go, what did I tell you? Endless fun for all the family, children's parties catered for … ***(Soldier 2 very carefully lifts a pair of clockwork teeth out of the case. He and Soldier 1 stare at them blankly)***… and you two look like the kind of lads who need a good laugh –

Soldier 1 ***(sharply)*** What?

Bunting I said: you two look like the kind of lads who need a good laugh.

Soldier 1 Laugh? Laugh? Laughing is banned by order of their magnificences Gilbert and Gloria Grimm ***(He points to the sign)***

Soldier Two, quote Presidential Decree number 13692, the Abolition of Cheerful Noises Act, Section 255, paragraph (b) …

Soldier 2 ***(mechanically)*** 'Any person suspected of having laughed or having committed the related offences of giggling, snickering, chuckling, whooping or whistling a happy tune will be handed over to the Chief of Secret police for severe punishment.'

Soldier 1 Thank you. Is this object supposed to encourage persons to make any of those noises?

Bunting Any? All. All my products are sure-fire side-splitters.

Soldier 1 Side-splitter? What's that then?

Bunting You know – a joke ***(Bunting mimes huge side-splitting laughter)*** Ho, ho, ho.

Soldier 2 What's that then?

Bunting You know: why did the chicken cross the road and all that.

Soldier 2 Why did what chicken cross what road?

Bunting To get to the other … ***(he stops and looks at them)*** This is a wind-up, isn't it? You've been having me on, haven't you? And I fell for it ***(He slaps his head and shakes it)*** Very good, very convincing, you almost had me believe you …

Soldier 1 ***(advances menacingly)*** A chicken tried to cross this border once, didn't it, Soldier Two?

Soldier 2 So we shot it.

Bunting ***(laughing)*** I can see you two are a riot when you get going.

Soldier 1 Do you know why we shot it?

Bunting ***(laughing)*** No … no, go on tell me, tell me.

Soldier 1 Tell him why we shot it, Soldier Two …

Soldier 2 Because we suspected it was a Cheerful Chicken …
(Bunting is convulsed with laughter)

Soldier 1 We have reason to believe you are also a cheerful person, Mr Bunting. Soldier Two, please quote Presidential Decree 65138: Immigration Control of Wandering Merrymakers and Sundry Funny Foreigners:

Soldier 2 'Shoot on sight.'

Soldier 1 By order of their grim and glorious magnificences, Gilbert and Gloria Grimm, we therefore execute you.

The Soldiers rapidly blindfold him.

Bunting Alright, boys, stop pratting around. A joke's a joke but you can take something too far.

They point their rifles at him.

Soldier 1 Ready …

Bunting You can't make me believe this is serious, you know …

Soldier 1 Aim …

Bunting *(aside)* Something tells me they might be serious. Best think quickly …

Soldier 1 Fi …

Bunting *(snatching off blindfold; in a different voice)* Excellent, gentlemen, you passed with flying colours. I shall pass on a glowing report about you to the Chief of Secret Police.

Soldier 1 The Chief of Secret Police?

Bunting This was only a test situation, mind you. In the real world, it could go many, many different ways. You may lower your rifles now.

Soldier 2 Only a test?

Bunting Yes, my lad.

Soldier 2 You mean you are an agent of our glorious secret police?

Bunting The most feared agent in your glorious secret police. ***(The Soldiers are instantly gripped with fear.)***

Soldier 1 How do we know you are an agent in the secret police?

Bunting Good man, I like that soldier. Sharp, alert, on the ball. ***(He looks round confidentially, lowers his voice)*** Have either of you ever heard of the Purple Monkey?

Soldier 2 No.

Bunting 'Course you haven't. Wouldn't be a very good secret agent if you had, would I? But who else but I, the Purple Monkey would dare to challenge the most feared border guards in the whole land?

Soldier 2 Who's that then?

Bunting You. The names of Soldier 1 and Soldier 2 have spread far and wide. I was sent by the Chief himself to find out if the stories were true. And now I can say, yes, it is an enormous honour for me to present you with this year's International Kill-Joy Award for outstanding achievement as a pair of miserable, boring gits.

Soldier 1 Thank you, sir.

Bunting ***(opening his case)*** Here, Soldier One, is your special souvenir kill-joy hat, nose and squeaker. ***(He takes them out his case)*** … Congratulations. Here Soldier Two are yours. Congratulations.

Soldier 1 I was right, Soldier Two. There was a special award.

Soldier 2 Yes, and we got it, Soldier One.

He shakes their hands as they put them on. They stand to attention and salute.

Bunting ***(aside)*** Aren't they a sad pair? No, aren't they though? It's the years out here, must've done something funny to their heads. Laws against laughter, they've got to be bonkers. Well, I can't hang around. I can't wait to see folks' faces fill with joy and for my pockets to fill with cash. Forward, Bob, to make your fortune …

He turns, salutes.

Keep up the excellent work, men.

Soldier 1 You can always rely on us, sir.

Bunting exits. Soldiers come to attention smartly and turn to face each other as if to march once up and down again. They catch sight of each other, blow their party squeakers in fright, yell, and run off in opposite directions.

2 THE CELL

The Book Years had ground by, grey, the same
Until the day that Bunting came,
Came a whisper, came a rumour
Of this salesman and his sense of humour
To the ears of those in power
Made them swear and glare and glower
For long ago their pride spoke thus:
'If you laugh, you laugh at us,
So all must be downcast by decree
To defend your leaders' dignity.'
And poor Bob Bunting, simple fool
Just danced upon their golden rule
His cheek must be denounced aloud
From their balcony to the crowd.

The page turns.

*A blast of loud triumphal music. A spotlight picks out the balcony of the Presidential Palace from which are waving **Gilbert Grimm, Gloria Grimm** and **Grizzelda Grimm**. On either side stands a bodyguard, **Mr Right** and **Mr Left**, each of whom holds a tape recorder. One is playing the music, on the other is the sound of the applause of an enthusiastic crowd.*

Gloria Keep waving Grizzelda.

Grizzelda But my arm aches, Mum.

Gilbert None of your lip, miss. Do as you're told.

Grizzelda But my arm is going to fall off, Dad.

Gloria A little pain for all this power. I've told you before, Grizzelda, you must learn the art of impressing a crowd.

Grizzelda I don't think it'll impress any of them if my arm falls off. Really impressive that'll be when my arm falls, crash, right into them. Oh yes, we three'll look so impressive standing up here with my arm somewhere down …

***Gilbert** slaps **Grizzelda**. She starts to cry.*

Well, why do I have to impress that bunch of losers down there anyway?

Gilbert Because we're showing the ordinary folk how extraordinary we are. Letting them gape at the cool, unflagging majesty of our extraordinary, endless waving. It's a symbol. It's a little peek at the endless power that you have if you're world leaders like me and your mother. And if you've got this kind of power, you don't hide it, you wave it about. It shows you're serious. It shows you don't stand for no funny business.

Gloria So shut your face and wave.

Gilbert Time for another big speech, I think. Mr Right, Mr Left, thank you. ***(The* bodyguards *turn off the music and applause.* Gilbert *and* Gloria *produce two megaphones)*** Ordinary folk, your attention please. Some very important good news just in from the State Statistics Department. Gloria?

Gloria Our glorious country's production of bath plugs has risen by one hundred and eighteen per cent.

A quick burst of taped applause.* The Grimms *wave.

Gloria We are now the greatest producer of bath plugs in the entire world.

A quick burst of taped applause.* The Grimms *wave.

Gilbert Another magnificent achievement all down to me, ordinary people. I, therefore, present myself with the Glorious Order of the Bath Plug First Class.

Gilbert* *pins a medal to his already overloaded uniform. A quick burst of taped applause.* The Grimms *wave.

Gloria Now some very important bad news just in. Gilbert?

Gilbert We have just heard that this man – ***(She displays a 'wanted' poster)*** – a man called Bobby Bunting has illegally entered our great and gloomy country with a suitcase full of jokes and novelties.

Another burst of taped applause. The Grimms stare at Mr Left who quickly turns off the tape recorder.

Mr Left Whoops, boss, sorry.

Gloria We want this man caught immediately.

Gilbert D'you think I'd have got as many medals on my chest today, if I kept on finding things funny?

Gloria Not blinking likely. Would we have shaken the world with the glory of our bath plugs if our glorious plug-makers had kept on knocking off for a bit of fun?

Gilbert No way. This man wants to chip away at our grumpiness. The grumpiness which has brought us greatness. That's why he must be caught.

Gloria And woe to any of you if you should find him even a little bit funny. The slightest snigger, the tiniest titter – and you're a foul traitor and you will have a bag shoved over your head and you will be chucked in prison!

Gilbert So I wouldn't if I were you. But if you catch him, your reward will be a glorious one:

Gloria The hand of our lovely daughter, Grizzelda, in marriage …

Grizzelda gawps. Taped applause.

Gilbert Yes the hand of Grizzelda

Gloria And half our republic!

Gilbert Oi, steady on. Just Grizzelda …

Gloria Alright, just Grizzelda. And my latest extremely expensive and totally unique handbag … ***(She holds it aloft. A surge of taped applause)***

Gilbert Signed …

Gloria … by both of us …

Gilbert To the man who brings Bobby Bunting in alive.

Gloria ***(to Gilbert)*** What if it's a woman?

Gilbert And if it's a woman …

Gloria … just the handbag …

Gilbert A fabulous reward indeed for catching the greatest threat to civilisation …

Gloria I shall now sing a glorious song of national praise

She launches horribly into song.

Marching, marching, marching
Boot-steps never bend
To our glorious future
Grim-faced till the –

Gilbert That's enough, thanks.

A burst of applause and triumphal music. Gilbert and Gloria leave the balcony followed by Mr Left and Mr Right.

Grizzelda Married? Did they just say married? But I don't want to get married. It's just not fair.

She burst into tears. Bunting appears from beneath the parapet of the balcony.

Bunting Allow me madam, to introduce myself. Wherever there is sadness and care, here I am to banish it. What seems to be the matter?

Grizzelda I'm not marrying just someone who catches the greatest threat to civilisation. I can't marry just anybody. I'm too young, special and famous.

Bunting Who is this greatest threat to civilisation?

Grizzelda ***(sniffs)*** Here, this is him. ***(She hands him the poster)***

Bunting Oh, now that looks like me, silly

Grizzelda ***(wipes her eyes)*** Yes, it does rather ***(she double-takes)*** Cripes, it's you, isn't it? ***(aside)*** Help, trapped on my own balcony with the greatest threat to civilisation. How did you get into the palace?

Bunting It's the only place where there's been no police around to chase me. What's going on in this country? Each place I come to, someone tells me they haven't laughed for twenty five years now. I say 'Great, you'll be wanting a party to celebrate and Bobby Bunting's the man to throw it'. A few hours later, everyone's having a lovely time and what happens? Swarms of police arrive; they shove bags on everyone's heads, chuck them all in the back of black vans and drive them away. Just between you and me: I'm beginning to suspect the government here have got something against people enjoying themselves. So, could you do me a big favour and point me to the fastest exit out of this stupid country?

Grizzelda Don't you know who I am? I am Grizzelda Grimm, daughter of Gilbert and Gloria Grimm who rule this country. And it's not stupid, actually.

Bunting Oh, great. That just tops everything off nicely, doesn't it? What a complete nightmare.

Grizzelda presses a button and an alarm sounds.

What's that?

Grizzelda My personal alarm. In three minutes my bodyguards will arrive and rescue me from your beastly clutches.

Bunting That was a bad move.

Grizzelda Why?

Bunting Well, if you remember, the first man to catch me gets to marry you.

Grizzelda So?

Bunting Do you really want to end up as Mrs Bodyguard? Is, if you'll 'scuse the pun, Mr Right your Mr Right?

Grizzelda Shut up, I'm thinking, shut up. What am I going to do? I can't think, I doomed.

She burst into tears.

Bunting There's no time for that. Listen, help me back across the border and you won't have to marry anyone, will you? You've got a choice: help me escape or marry a nobody.

Grizzelda *(stops quickly)* We'll have to jump.

Bunting Jump? How? It's miles down.

Grizzelda That's easy. For when I was just three years old my Mum and Dad had my hair cunningly extended to the length of fifty feet and industrially strengthened to a breaking strain of 800 pounds thus enabling them to escape from high buildings in case of fire, bomb-scare, revolution, or other such dire emergency … ***(Bunting looks baffled)*** Is there anything weird about that?

Bunting No, no. It's very handy.

Grizzelda unravels her hair over the balcony.

Mr Left *(off)* Quick Mr Right …

Grizzelda Hurry, they're coming ***(Bunting begins climbing down her hair)*** Ow, watch it, have you any idea how much reinforced steel pigtails cost?

Bunting *(climbing down out of sight)* Sorry.

Grizzelda Hang on. How am I going to get down?

Bunting *(off)* Mum and Dad obviously didn't think about that. You'll have to jump. I'll catch you.

Grizzelda Promise?

Bunting *(off)* Scout's honour ***(She jumps. A crash)*** Never was a good enough catcher for the Scouts.

*The **bodyguards** arrive on the balcony.*

Mr Right What's happened Mr Left?

Mr Left It's Miss Grizzelda, Mr Right. She's been stolen by the Cheerful One.

*The **Grimms** arrive on the balcony.*

Gilbert What's the matter? Where's Grizzelda?

Mr Right She's been kidnapped, boss.

Gloria Kidnapped? Who by?

Mr Left Guess, boss …

Gloria Not …

Gilbert Bobby Bunting?!

Gloria Mobilise the army!

Gilbert Launch the navy!

Gloria Unleash the alsatians!

Bodyguards Yes, boss *(They run off)*

Gilbert We want him sniffed out!

Gloria We want him flushed out!

Gilbert We want a bag shoved on his head!

Gloria And him in prison forever …

Alarms go off everywhere.

3 THE CELL

The Book So Bunting took the girl and ran
Now he's the land's most wanted man
Headlines scream GET BOBBY THE BAD
HE'S SWIPED OUR GRIZZ FROM MUM AND DAD
Who will win this worthy quest
And stand the hero from the rest?
Soldiers One and Two gave chase,
Traced them to the self-same place
Where two grey women come to meet
Every day on the self-same seat
In the self-same park where years before
They lost their children to the law
For some news, some clue to their fate
Two sad mothers wait and wait.

The page turns.

A park, empty except for a concrete bench and a concrete litter bin. A sign which says THIS PARK IS NOT FOR THE ENJOYMENT OF LOCAL PEOPLE.

Silence.

Dull appears. She carries a brown paper bag. She looks at her watch, looks shiftily around and waits. Pause. Dismal appears, also carrying a brown paper bag.

Dull ***(dully)*** Hello, Mrs Dismal.

Dismal ***(dismally)*** Hello.

Their eyes move shiftily to the left and then to the right and then to each other. Then they move quickly to the bench and sit.

Dull ***(deliberately as if to be overheard)*** Shall we feed the ducks, Mrs Dismal?

Dismal ***(also deliberately as if to be overheard)*** We only ever come here to feed the ducks, Mrs Dull, don't we?

They start picking breadcrumbs out of their bags and tossing it in front of them.

Dull Nice and quiet, then …

Dismal Very nice and quiet …

Dull No one about, then …

Dismal Not a soul.

Dull Another dull and dismal day.

Dismal Same as always …

Bunting and Grizzelda run past yelling.

Dull Did you feel something brush past then?

Dismal When?

Bunting and Grizzelda run past again, yelling.

Dull Then.

Dismal No, Mrs Dull. Not a thing.

Dull No, nor me.

Dismal As you know, Mrs Dull, in our gloriously uneventful country, one day things are here the next they're not. It's the custom.

Dull Exactly, it's routine. You take no notice, you don't remember.

Dismal Exactly. I don't notice anything.

Dull For instance, do you remember in this park we had flowers and trees once?

Dismal No.

Dull Nor me. Or that one day we had swings and slides, the next – bang – gone?

Dismal No.

Dull Nor me. Or that one day we brought sandwiches to the park with our boys, just as usual, and I saw a pretty duck fly over and I pointed and said 'Look, Mrs Dismal' and then, all of a sudden, it was very quiet here?

Dismal Every day has been very quiet here, Mrs Dull.

Dull Yes. Every day has been the same as always.

*The **Soldiers** run on.*

Dismal Quick, Soldiers, Mrs Dull. Pretend to feed the ducks.

They begin frantically tossing bread.

Soldier 1 And try not to mess things up this time Soldier Two. This is our big chance. We could win this fabulous reward and marry Grizzelda.

Soldier 2 He won't give us the slip this time, Soldier One. You can have her half the year. I'll have her the other half.

*They run off. **Bunting and Grizzelda** come back.*

Bunting I think we've shaken them off.

Grizzelda I want to go home.

Bunting So do I. And until I am out of this stupid country …

Grizzelda It's not …

Bunting *It's a very stupid country* and until I'm out of it, we're in this together.

Grizzelda *(aside)* What a ludicrous situation for the most important little girl in the world. *(to Bunting)* I hate you *(she starts crying)*

Bunting Blimey, you're always blubbering.

Grizzelda Well, I'm hungry. Those ordinary folk have got sandwiches. I want one of their sandwiches.

Bunting Well, ask for one then.

Grizzelda Oh yes, of course. I, Grizzelda Grimm, can just breeze up to two nobodies in the park and ask for a sandwich. Don't you realise I'm instantly recognisable?

Bunting And my face is plastered across every wall and every screen and every newspaper …

Grizzelda Listen you may be the greatest threat to civilisation but I'm still more of a celebrity than you …

Bunting Alright, you better put on a disguise then. ***(He gets one out of his suitcase. She puts it on.)***

Grizzelda How do I look?

Bunting Your own mother wouldn't know …

Grizzelda Leave my wonderful mother out of this. Don't you dare mention my mother.

Grizzelda goes up to Dismal and Dull.

Grizzelda *(putting on what she thinks is an ordinary person's voice)* Hello, ordinary persons. I'm another ordinary person. Give us a sandwich.

Dull *(whispers)* That's a very unusual person, Mrs Dismal

Dismal *(whispers)* Take no notice, Mrs Dull.

Grizzelda *(shouts)* Are you stupid? I said I want a sandwich.

Dismal *(defensively)* We're feeding the ducks with them.

Dull We only come here to feed the ducks.

Grizzelda Well, you are stupid then. 'Cos there aren't any ducks. There's been no ducks for ages. So give us a sandwich.

Dull Do you know what happened to the ducks by any chance?

Grizzelda I can't tell you. It's top secret.

Dismal We'll give you a sandwich if you tell.

Grizzelda Oh alright, they were all arrested ages ago for laughing at my Da – the President. They had been infiltrated by foreign agents. What about that sandwich then?

Dull And is that what happened to all the other things that disappeared?

Grizzelda No, I'm not allowed. It's very top secret.

Dismal ***(holding it up)*** Nice, big, juicy sandwich …

Grizzelda Alright, everything was arrested. The flowers, the ducks and the trees, everything looked far too cheerful. That's what gave them away. They were all foreign agents in disguise. ***(She takes a sandwich)***

Dull So you don't know anything about any children then?

Grizzelda Children? What children? No, I don't know anything about children.

Dull You don't know where they ended up then?

Grizzelda ***(shrugs)*** Might have been the same place as the ducks, I suppose.

Dismal Where was that?

Grizzelda ***(bites into the sandwich)*** The sandwich spread factory.

Dismal and Dull burst into tears.

Bunting You know how to say just the right thing, don't you?

Grizzelda You don't understand anything do you? It's quite simple: being cheerful is absolutely against the law here. I expect their children were infiltrated by foreign agents too. I don't have any sympathy. Not my fault is it, if the ordinary folk can't bring up their children properly …

Dismal and Dull start crying on Grizzelda.

Grizzelda Oh no, do something. They'll ruin my frock.

Bunting Let me introduce myself, ladies, Bobby Bunting, salesman of top quality jokes and novelties. ***(He shakes hands with Dismal and Dull. An electric shock. They stand stunned.)***

Dismal … Do that again … ***(He does it again. A dreamy smile drifts across her face.)*** I remember that. My little Derek used to play that one on me.

Dull … And my little Eric on me … Do it again ***(He does it again. they start laughing. They stop laughing, very shocked.)*** Do it again ***(He does it again to both of them.)***

Dismal and Dull ***(laughing, to each other)*** Remember that?

Dismal … Oh yes. And you remember the time he … ***(laughing)***

Dull … Yes, yes when they both … ***(They laugh uproariously, slapping the bench. Dull points at Grizzelda in her disguise.)*** Look at her. ***(They howl with laughter. Dismal falls of the bench laughing.)***

Grizzelda Are they laughing at me? You made them laugh at me. Do you know who I am? I am Grizzelda Grimm, the President's daughter.

Dismal ***(laughing)*** 'Course you are.

Dull ***(laughing)*** Tell us another one.

Grizzelda Police! Police! Help! Help! You're all for it. Police! Police!

Bunting Oh no, they're coming. Now you've done it. If one of them catches me, you'll have to marry him …

Grizzelda But I've got my disguise. They won't know who I am.

Bunting picks up his suitcase and runs. The Soldiers run on.

It's the Cheerful One. Look, he's struck again. ***(She points at Dismal and Dull)*** He went that way. ***(Soldiers run off quickly. Pause. Then they stroll back towards Grizzelda threateningly. Dismal and Dull are strewn around the park, breathless.)***

Soldier 1 And who are you exactly?

Grizzelda Me? Why, I'm – I'm just a very ordinary little girl – who – who was taking a stroll in the park and came across a terrible crime being committed so I did my duty.

Soldier 1 Proof of identity, please, ordinary little girl.

Grizzelda ***(she pretends to fumble)*** Oh dear, seem to have lost it.

Soldier 2 That's very convenient.

Soldier 1 It's you again, isn't it? Bobby Bunting in another ridiculous disguise. Well, we're not so easily fooled this time.

Grizzelda ***(shouts)*** Listen, I'm just a very ordinary little girl who just happened to be in the park and who's done nothing wrong so back off, Soldier.

Soldier 1 You're under arrest.

Grizzelda No, no. Wait, wait. You're making a terrible mistake! I'm innocent!

Soldier 1 How many times have I heard that before, Soldier Two?

Soldier 2 Three hundred and sixty two times, Soldier One.

Soldier 1 Come on. I'm going to collect my reward, Soldier Two. You deal with those two.

He exits with Grizzelda.

Grizzelda No, I'm not him, he's him, I'm me. I'm just an ordinary little girl …

Soldier 2 ***(coming to attention)*** Presidential Decree 254167: Forbidding All Public Displays of Heartiness and Outdoor Jollification. Paragraph 52, subsection (b) Offenders shall be bagged, coshed and handed over to the security forces. ***(Dull is in the bin, trying not to laugh. Dismal is under the bench.)*** Don't you see, ladies, laughing in a park is a very serious offence? I'm only carrying out orders.

Dull We only come here to feed the ducks.

Soldier 2 Give me your bags.

He takes their sandwich bags and puts them over their heads. He brings out a truncheon. He stops, looks round and hides it behind his back. He shouts round the park.

What was that? A truncheon? Was it? No. A large sausage, it was. It's a little known and much misunderstood custom in this country for members of the armed forces to tap ordinary women lightly about the head with a large sausage.

He hits them each on the head very hard. They slump.

I told you it was much misunderstood.

4 THE CELL

The Book To the cells went poor Grizzelda
Seven days and nights they held her
Till Bunting cried and caused a stir
'You've got it wrong, it isn't her!'
The shocked police stared in wonder
As he bravely showed their blunder
(For here it was quite unknown
To go down the station on your own)
And though locked up, still Bunting thought
'Perhaps it's best that I've been caught
My trial will cut this tangled knot
And sort the guilty from the not.'

The page turns.

A blast of loud triumphal music. ***Gloria*** *and* ***Gilbert*** *appear on high with megaphones.*

Gilbert Alright, pay attention, ordinary folk. Despite our warnings you're continuing to enjoy yourselves. Now we won't stand for any more of this. Any more reported outbreaks of laughter and it's bags on heads all round.

Gloria Do you think that when the peace and security of the nation is threatened we muck about?

Gilbert That we would stand by while a madman goes bonkers through our streets? That the maintenance of law and order isn't a top priority of the Grimms?

Gloria That we are not, in fact, a proper pair of leaders? You are about to see that we are!

Gilbert Ladies and gentlemen, boys and girls, we present the trial of Mr Bobby Bunting.

Gloria It's going to be *fair.*

Gilbert It's going to be *free.*

Gloria And it's going to be *thoroughly educational* …

Gilbert Fling wide the doors of the Great Court. Let Justice be seen to be well and truly done …

Another blast of loud triumphal music. They disappear and The Great Court ofJustice appears. Everything is covered in dust and cobwebs. Slumped in a chair is a skeleton. ***Soldiers*** *enter with* ***Bunting.*** *He has a bag over his head.*

Bunting Take the bag off now then.

Soldier 1 We can't do that, son.

Soldier 2 You have to be proved innocent first. Sit down.

They push him into the dock.

Bunting But I'm innocent until proven guilty, isn't that right?

Soldier 2 Oh no, you've got that the wrong way round. Guilty until proven innocent.

Bunting Right, I want to see my lawyer.

Soldier 1 He wants to see his lawyer, Soldier Two.

Soldier 2 Well you can't see him but here he is.

Bunting Who is he?

Soldier 1 He's the best defence lawyer that could be found.

Bunting *(whispers to the skeleton)* Hello? Hello? What do you reckon to my chances then? What do you do when you think a law is ridiculous? Just to sort everything out, I think I should just go along with their funny legal traditions ***(He points to the bag)*** … don't you? … but … oh but what have I got to worry about? No court in the world would condemn me, would they? Hello, can you hear me? Hello?

Soldier 2 Silence in court. Ladies and gentlemen, be upstanding please for their honours the two Lord Chief Justices …

***Gilbert** and **Gloria** enter dressed as judges. Soldiers stand the skeleton up.*

(to Soldier 1) But aren't they …? Isn't she …?

Soldier 1 Take no notice, Soldier Two. Do you want to get us in to even more trouble? We've jury duty to do.

Soldiers go into the jury box.

Gilbert *(impersonating a venerable judge)* Humph-mumph, the accused will stand to hear the charge. ***(Bunting stands.)***

Bobby Bunting you are charged that you did smuggle into this country a quantity of jokes and novelties with the intention of causing complete hysteria. Ahem, furthermore, that you are thus a crazed terrorist in the pay of our foreign enemies bent on overthrowing our lovely government. How do you plead?

Bunting Not guilty of course.

Gloria *(as if she misheard)* Not guilty?

Bunting Yes.

Gloria Ahem, fine.

Gilbert Members of the jury?

A Jury of Puppets appears in the jury box. They are worked by the soldiers!

Gilbert Now you are a jury made up of twelve honest, decent and true individuals – you are twelve, honest decent and true individuals, aren't you?

Jury *(in chorus)* Yes, yes, your honour.

Gilbert It is your duty to freely judge the guilt – or innocence – of this man you see before you.

Gloria Now we must ask you: are you being influenced by any outside force you can think of which might swing your judgement one way or the other?

Jury No, no, your honour.

Gilbert Then all is in order. Call the first witnesses.

Gloria The State calls Mrs Dismal and Mrs Dull.

Dismal and Dull come in. Gloria takes the bags off their heads.

Do you swear that all you shall say in this court will be nothing but the truth?

Both Erm – yes.

Gloria Are you Dull and are you Dismal?

Both We are.

Dull And aren't you …?

Dismal Ssh, Mrs Dull. Take no notice.

Gloria Where were you a week ago?

Dismal We were in the park feeding the ducks.

Dull We only go to the park to feed the ducks.

Gloria And then what happened?

Dismal Suddenly this man …

Gloria *(points suddenly at Bunting)* *This* man?

Dismal Yes ***(points likewise at Bunting)*** that man – sat down next to us on the bench, nudged my companion and whispered – and whispered – go on …

Dull Me?

Gloria Yes, Mrs Dull, tell the court what he whispered to you.

Dull Errr – ***(She struggles to remember what she has been told to say …)*** He nudged me and whispered …

Dismal *(whispers to her)* Psst, tell them what the police officer with the big hands told you to say …

Dull *(aloud)* He whispered: 'Psst, tell them what the police officer with the big hands told you to say ...'

Dismal No! he didn't say that.

Dull He didn't?

Dismal No, he said, 'Here, look at my lovely fun-packed suitcase ...'

Dull Who, the police officer with the big hands?

Dismal ***(pointing at Bunting)*** No, him, he said that, remember 'Look at my lovely fun-packed suitcase full ... of ...' Remember?

Dull ***(remembers with a rush)*** Oh yes, he said 'Here, look at my lovely fun-packed suitcase, full of the latest comics and joke books and toys from abroad. Your kiddies will love them. And you'll be doing your bit to bring about the fall of the government too. Go on, take a peek. You know you want to ...'

A low moan from the Jury.

Jury What a swine.

What a snake-in-the-grass.

Bunting That's untrue!

Gilbert Silence in court.

Gloria ***(to Mrs Dull)*** Did you reply?

Dismal Oh yes, ***(she gestures melodramatically)*** I said: 'You know what you can do with your horrid suitcase? You can throw it in the gutter where it belongs ...'

Jury Well said ...

Bravo ...

Nice one ...

Dismal 'What madness to think we would even look at your dangerous propaganda and weird objects! These crazy rags are a nasty stain on our pure fun-free society! We know all too well the price of tolerating your barmy ideas, you evil foreigner ...' ***(getting carried away)*** And it's true, ladies and gentlemen, we lost our children, we're told, because they had been infiltrated by foreign agents cunningly disguised as ducks ...'

Gilbert Thank you, Mrs Dismal.

Dismal ... but by doing our duty today we hope we might get them back ...

Gilbert You can sit down now …

Jury Sit down, sit down, shut up …

Dismal Look, we have a piece of paper signed by the President promising to look in to the matter of our missing children if we …

Gilbert This is a court of law. ***(He snatches the paper)*** The President has no authority here at all. Please sit down.

Jury Sit down, sit down …

Dismal … if we only stood up and spoke out against …

Gilbert Shut your gob! ***(as Judge)*** I mean, silence in court.

Bunting Nobbled, they've been nobbled …

Gloria Nobbled? Explain yourself, Mr Bunting.

Jury Explain …

Bunting They've been bribed. They've been bribed to give false evidence against me in return for information about their children. Everything they just said was lies.

Dull ***(stands)*** It's true … ***(Dismal pulls her back down.)***

Gloria ***(sharply)*** What's true?

Dull Nothing …

Dismal Everything. Everything we just said was true.

Bunting But they told me that their children had disappeared in the park.

Gloria Disappeared, Mr Bunting? When do children just disappear? It would appear you're living in a fairy tale world. It would appear you believe our public parks are a place for magic tricks instead of somewhere quiet for our ordinary folk to reflect seriously about how wonderful it is to live here. It would appear you are *not a very serious person.* I would take note of that when considering your verdict, members of the jury.

Jury make thoughtful, noting noises.

Please go on Mrs Dull. When you refused his offer of the comic items did he become … aggressive in any way?

Dull Aggressive? ***(She gets out a card from her bag, holds it out of sight and reads from it)*** … Oh yes. At this, Bobby Bunting became very angry and got out a bun …

Dismal ***(looks at card)*** Gun.

Dull Gun. Having first subjected us to a series of violent electric smocks – shocks – which caused us to briefly lose our self-control, he then put our sandwich bags over our heads and cruelly knocked us out with his bun. We remember nothing after that.

Dismal Though we have the cruel bruises to this very day …

They sit. Dull stands

Dull Though the police were very kind throughout. ***(She sits.)***

Bunting ***(laughing in spite of himself)*** Your honours, this is all getting silly – you can't really believe this …

Gloria Oh, Mr Bunting, so you think torture and violence are just silly. Is it one of your jokes to terrify two poor defenceless women? Very telling, members of the jury, very telling.

Jury ***(to each other)*** Very telling, very telling.

Bunting But it's lies. They're telling lies.

Gilbert Mrs Dismal and Mrs Dull, I want you to think very carefully before you answer this question. It could have very serious consequences for you. Or, indeed, anyone *at all connected* with you. Now, please answer freely and truthfully – we want the truth.

Jury The truth! The truth! Yes, the truth.

Gilbert Have you been lying to this court?

Bunting Please …

Dull and **Dismal** ***(finally, miserably)*** No.

Gilbert Thank you.

Dismal ***(stands up suddenly)*** But we did have a piece of paper signed by the President and where *are* our Derek and Eric?

Gloria Bag on head! Bag on head, now!

Dismal and Dull cower back under their bags.

Ahem, no further questions.

Gilbert Let us proceed. Call the final witness. The State calls Grizzelda Grimm.

Grizzelda enters, she takes her place in the witness box.

Gloria Are you Grizzelda Grimm?

Grizzelda I am.

Gloria What were you doing on the balcony of the Presidential Palace a week ago?

Grizzelda I was waving.

Gloria And then what happened?

Grizzelda Suddenly this man appeared …

Gloria ***(points accusingly at Bunting)*** *This* man … ?

Grizzelda Yes, that man. He told me that he had been spreading light, laughter and joy across the land and then he violently took me hostage.

The Jury is outraged.

Jury Desperado!
Send him down!
Put him away!
Cut big bits of him off!

Bunting I object …

Gloria Members of the jury let us not get carried away by emotion …

Jury ***(shouting)*** No!

Gloria … but let us look at the evidence calmly, coolly, on balance …

Jury ***(shouting)*** Yes!

Gloria Mr Bunting?

Bunting Well, it's not true I kidnapped her. She came of her own accord …

Jury Shut up
Boo!
Rubbish.

Gilbert Well, now whom do we believe? Do we believe she would go freely with a man who, *it may be* steals the minds of our young ones with his filthy ragbag of toys …?

Jury He's a naughty brainwasher …

Gloria Do we believe she would just go for a little stroll with a man who, *perhaps,* terrifies poor defenceless women so badly that they think their children have suddenly become invisible …?

Jury And a thug!

And a hooligan!
A crazed low thing!!

Gilbert Do we believe she would exchange idle chit-chat with a man who, *it could very well be*, cheerfully whips the normally sensible folk of this land up into a complete frenzy with his riotous parties full of loud music with its wicked foreign rhythms …?

Jury Wicked! Wicked! He's a wicked rabble-rouser!

Gloria Finally, do we believe that this man is, under this disguise of a travelling salesman, the evil spawn of the Happy Ones, in league with the dark forces of cheerfulness; in short, a fanatic funster who would snatch this girl to blackmail her parents into bringing back those bad old days of nationwide frivolity …?

Gilbert Or do we believe this little sunbeam of innocent girlhood? This nice-smelling flower of our proud nation state? Tell us, Grizzelda. Tell us the truth about your ordeal, if you can bear it …

Jury The truth! The truth! Tell us the truth!

Grizzelda My ordeal? Well, how long I was held for I don't remember. I didn't know where I was. Nobody told me anything for ages. Then they said I was at the police station. What am I – the most important little girl – doing at the police station, I asked? Nobody answered. They put me in a cell down a long, long corridor full of doors. The lights were very bright. They never went out. I didn't know whether it was day or night. Of course, I thought, someone will notice, someone will remember who I am, someone will come and find me, but nobody did. I tried to sleep but I was woken up by a noise. It was the shuffling of feet. I went to the little spy-hole in my door and I saw little people all with bags over their heads. Little people being marched past, away down the corridor into darkness. I tried to look one way but I couldn't see the beginning of the line. And I looked the other way but I couldn't see the end of it. It just went on and on, never stopping. 'Who are they all'? I shouted to the guard. 'The enemies of the State. These children must be taken away for their own protection and to protect their magnificences. They're going to learn how to be serious people.' I asked where but the guard wouldn't answer. So where were they going, dad? What had they done? And something else I don't understand. If you're so magnificent, mum: why do you need to be protected from children?

A stunned silence.

Gloria Grizzelda!

Gilbert She's blown it …

Gloria That wasn't what you were supposed to say …

Gilbert I do not believe it. She's blinking blown it …

Grizzelda I'm sorry Dad. It just sort of slipped out. I'm sorry, Mum.

Bunting Dad? Mum? What's going on here? ***(He begins to struggle out of the bag)***

Dismal Is that true? That it's you that takes the children?

Dull Shame.

Jury Shame, shame, boo –

Gloria Silence in court! Members of the jury, we want a sentence right now.

Dismal Well, frankly, Dilys and I think you're the guilty ones …

Jury Yes, yes, guilty! Guilty! Guilty

Gilbert Silence! We will have silence!

Bunting ***(struggles out of the bag, he looks round)*** Well, I'll be jiggered …

Gilbert Have you no respect for law and order?

Gloria You don't deserve justice, you anarchists!

Jury ***(football chant)*** Guil-ty! Guil-ty! Guil-ty!

Gilbert Silence before your leaders. Shut up or I'll have you all in the Graveyard for Not Very Important Dead People by the morning …

Silence slowly spreads.

(to Bunting) And you, put that bag back over your head before I knock it off for you.

Bunting But I want to confess.

Gloria You do?

Bunting Oh yes … Members of the jury, ladies and gentlemen. I came to this country an ordinary Joe, a young man seeking his fortune. Laughter is my trade. Oh yes, it's true, I am cheerful. And I wandered cheerfully into this place like a toddler in to traffic. And now I realise how wrong I was, how very, very wrong. Unfortunately, this trial has turned out a bit wrong too. I think – and this is just the personal opinion, mind you – it's all turned out a *bit of a joke.* And I think it's on – you two – so ha, ha, ha, ha …

Gilbert That's it, I'm going to smash his face in.

***Gilbert** attacks Bunting.*

Gloria Gilbert, not in public …

*The **Soldiers** rush to help.*

Ordinary people, we apologise for the temporary loss of law and order. It will be resumed as soon as possible. In the meantime, here is a song:

Sleep peaceful little babe,
Under the watchful gaze of Grimm –

Gilbert *(struggling)* Oh yes, Gloria, just the time for you to start screeching like a skidding truck.

Gloria *What? What? My voice is so unlike a skidding truck, it is so unlike that …*

***Gloria** attacks Gilbert. Everyone is fighting and then a strange noise is heard. **Bunting** struggles up and points at Grizzelda.*

Bunting Look, look, she's laughing. She's laughing.

Everything stops and they all stare at Grizzelda. She puts her hand over her mouth and looks astonished.

5 THE CELL

The Book When Grizzelda, once so proud
Broke the law and laughed out loud
Her laugh was echoed by a choir
And rebellion spread like wild fire
Their plot foiled by their own daughter
Forgetting lies that they had taught her
The Grimms, who hated any failures,
Sent the Soldiers as Bunting's jailers
To a distant prison which was for
Persistent breakers of their law.

The page turns.

The exercise yard of the Prison for Chronic Comedians

Soldier 1 ***(offstage: shouts)*** Exercise squad number 67, attention! One, two, one, two … ***(Soldier 1 marches on a line of Prisoners)*** … Halt! Get into line! Face front! ***(They shuffle into place)*** Well, life has really gobbed in my eye this time, hasn't it? I can't tell you how very, very grumpy it makes me to have ended up guarding you lot. Long term, unrepentant, persistent comedians – all the slops of every tacky night club gutter, sleazy cabaret and tinselly den of amusement. The prison doctor will tell you that you can be cured. But I say, no, no … ***(He glowers at them)*** I say, a leopard cannot change its socks.

A snigger is heard.

What was that? Did I say something funny? Did I say anything funny? I don't think I did.

He marches up and down the line.

What is it with you, eh? You are in a ferociously guarded top security prison miles from anywhere for a very, very long time. I think we can say your situation is *not funny, not funny at all*, yes?

Prisoner 1 ***(advances)*** Well, you know, actually, sir, that reminds me of a little story that …

Soldier 1 *Shut up. Get back into line.* You with your little stories, and your catchphrases, and your funny things happening on the way to everywhere. *God I hate you. Shut up* … Now, in five minutes you have your thought-provoking breakfast lecture from Doctor Bleach …

Grumbles from the Comedians.

But before that we're going to do some of my good, old-fashioned walking in boring, miserable circles. Walking in circles, by the right, go!

Prisoners begin to trudge round in circles. Soldier 2 marches on Bunting who joins the exercise squad. The Soldiers talk apart.

Soldier 2 I'm worried, Soldier One. Twenty more comedians arrived yesterday, another truckload this morning with a troupe of jugglers, two parties of very witty dinner guests and an amusing talking parrot. Where's it going to end?

Soldier 1 Now Bobby Bunting's here out of harm's way, it'll all die down. Once they realise we're going to use all means necessary to keep everyone in line, all these trouble-makers will just disappear, you'll see.

Soldier 2 All means necessary? What does that mean? What do we have to do, Soldier 1?

Soldier 1 Anything – necessary. That's our job.

Soldier 2 What like bully and threaten them? ***(shouts)*** *Walk in better circles you scum or else!* ***(to Soldier 1)*** Like that?

Soldier 1 Like that, yes, that's good, and …

Soldier 2 And?

Soldier 1 Anything else that's necessary. Come, Soldier Two. They're comedians, remember? They're not proper human beings, you know …

He marches off. Soldier 2 stands looking out. A Comedian sidles up to Bunting.

Prisoner 2 New then are you?

Bunting ***(nods)*** What are you in for?

Prisoner 2 Stand-up comedy. Might have heard of me, Norman 'Chuckles' Glee? Or my catchphrase 'That's all true that is'? ***(pause)*** No, well, it was twenty-five years ago. I was very popular then …

Bunting You've been in here twenty-five years?

Prisoner 2 One of the first to be arrested, I was. When the Grimms came to power and they sent the police round to the theatres and clubs to arrest all the comics. See those two over there? ***(He points to two prisoners who look strangely like Gilbert and Gloria)*** They used to impersonate the Grimms. ***(The pair smile and wave)*** Not very well, mind. But it didn't matter; they arrested us all, bad or good. The police bring me in, my interrogator sits me down, gives me a cup of tea 'so, you're a stand-up comic, then?' and says, 'you've been banned. This is a warning, you're free to go now, but if you perform any part of your routine, you're for it'. So I get up from the table, and he says 'You're under arrest'. 'Why'? I said. 'You're standing up', he said. ***(cheerfully)*** That's all true, that is. ***(Face drops …)*** And it is. And here I am, for twenty five years …

Bunting ***(outraged)*** Didn't your fans campaign for you?

Prisoner 3 ***(butts in)*** What fans?

Prisoner 2 I had loads of fans, me, that is until I was put in here. But who's going to be a fan when you're locked away? That's what you learn here. You don't stand up anymore. You keep your head down …

Bunting But that's giving in. If we stick together …

Prisoner 3 Face it, Glee. You never had no fans. You never had no fans because you were never funny …

Prisoner 2 And you were about as funny as this punch in the mouth I'm going to give you …

***Prisoner 2** makes a leap for **Prisoner 3**. **Soldier 1** returns carrying a bunch of bananas.*

Soldier 1 What's going on, Soldier Two, you were supposed to be guarding them? ***(Soldiers** break up the fight.)* I warned you, didn't I? Comedians: put them together in a confined space and they're like wild animals. All of you lot, back into line … Prepare to receive your breakfast banana. Prepare for Doctor Bleach's instructive lecture.

***Soldier 1** hands each Prisoner a banana. **Doctor** comes in.*

Doctor Hello, everyone, hello. Another day has dawned on your long road to your recovery. Now before I begin, everyone should meet, Prisoner Bunting. A most interesting case. It's said you have an irrepressible sense of humour. ***(Doctor** looks grave)* Is that so?

Bunting Ha, ha, ha, yes.

Doctor Rubbish! Why is that rubbish, everyone?

Prisoners *(in chorus)* Because there is no such thing as a sense of humour.

Doctor Correct. It makes it sound natural and logical and sensible to call it a 'sense', doesn't it?

Bunting Yes.

Doctor But humour is not a sense, Prisoner Bunting, oh no. It is a psycho-social deformity. And every one of you, alas, has it, don't you? What do you have?

Prisoners A psycho-social deformity.

Bunting What's that mean?

Doctor Can anyone tell Prisoner Bunting?

Prisoner 4 *(casually, to Bunting)* It means we're mad.

Doctor Correct. You may begin your bananas. This morning's lecture is entitled 'You: the Clown – a menace to society'.

*The **Soldiers** bring on a blackboard on which is chalked a drawing of a* *clown. **Doctor** slaps the board with a pointer.*

This is a clown. A bizarre-looking person. Some would say wacky – I do not. Face – smeared in a thick layer of coloured grease. Nose – obviously not their own. Trousers – illogically and unmanageably large. Normal people do not dress like this. Normal people do not fall over as much as this. Normal people do not hurl platefuls of their pudding at one another. Why do it? Because some terrifying urge compels them – and indeed all of you comedians – to constantly dress up and behave stupidly and inflict your stupidity on a sane and ordered society. And it is my solemn vow to cure this, your terrible habit. Any questions?

Bunting Yes, why do we have to eat bananas?

Doctor You eat bananas because I have noted your behaviour to be similar to our hairy friends from farther down the evolutionary scale. *(The **Doctor** hops up and down once or twice)* Hoo, hoo, hoo, haa, haa, haa, etcetera. Isn't that just like a comedian?

Bunting Well, I think that as an impersonation it needs a little ...

Doctor Be quiet. So, until you can behave like proper human beings it's bananas for breakfast, and bananas for lunch, dinner and supper ...

Bunting And bananas dancing on our duckdown duvets all through the night ...

Doctor Hoo, hoo, hoo, haa, haa, haa. Only the mad and monkeys want to laugh at everything, Prisoner Bunting. But you comics have an even worse madness. You want to make other people laugh too. You want to spread your madness. You don't want people to face up to real life. And what is real life but a very unhappy business. What is real life?

Prisoners A very unhappy business.

***Bunting** drops his banana skin ...*

Doctor Oh, yes it is. That is why you are here; that is why I am here. For it is my job to see to it that you accept real life for what it is. Miserably cruel and endlessly depressing. And do not fear, for with my treatment I shall lead you all triumphantly, magnificently in to light. Forward, friends, to the real world!

***Doctor** slips on the banana skin. **Bunting** laughs. The **Prisoners** edge back in fear from him, muttering.*

Bunting *(stops laughing)* Oh, come on you lot. Alright it's an old joke but it's not that bad … Listen, if we don't stick together in this, they'll …

Doctor This is the worst case of chronic comic tendency I have ever seen. Prisoner Bunting must be put in solitary confinement, Soldier Two. Ensure there is no light in the cell.

Soldier 2 Isn't that a bit harsh, Doctor?

Soldier 1 A bit harsh? This is a prison, Soldier Two, not some cosy little hospital.

Doctor No, Soldier One, it is a hospital. And this man is very, very sick. He must be separated for his own protection and the protection of the others. I feel if I can cure this man I can cure anyone. And I shall see to it personally that I do. Miserably cruel and endlessly depressing, Prisoner Bunting. That's what life is.

They take him away.

6 THE CELL

The Book In a frenzy of rediscovered fun
People came together as one
As they gather against the gloom,
And time ticks by and crisis looms
The Grimms are victims of a mood
They hear that jokes are in their food
By crunching lunch or gobbling tea
They'll be struck stone dead by a novelty.
Two tasters then must test each piece
Of every dish at every feast,
Prospects bad and the pay's abysmal,
Who got the job? Dull and Dismal.

The page turns.

A dark and gloomy room with thick curtains. A very long breakfast table with candles. At one end sits Gilbert looking grumpy. A fanfare. Gloria enters yawning and sits at the other end.

Gloria *(produces megaphone)* Good morning dear.

Gilbert *(produces his megaphone)* What's good about it?

Gloria Nothing.

Gilbert We've got an outbreak of dancing in the north, a fun-fair has been spotted in the east, a pantomime horse is running riot all over the south and I distinctly heard a muffled chortle in my bath this morning. We're surrounded by happy, laughing enemies. So what's good about it?

Gloria Nothing, I said, nothing.

Gilbert So why don't you shut up then?

Gloria Why don't you?

A sulky pause.

Gloria We've done everything. We've bullied them, we've threatened them. We've bagged anyone with even a smirk on their face. We've packed the prisons to bursting. So why does everyone still think we're so funny?

Gilbert I don't know.

Gloria What are we going to do? Let's consult the manual for unbearably strict world leaders.

Gilbert opens it.

Gilbert It says to behave completely as if nothing was wrong or has ever been wrong. As if everything was completely normal.

Gloria Right. ***(shouts off)*** Dismal, Dull? ***(Dismal and Dull appear)*** Order me another three dozen totally unique handbags.

Gilbert And bring me three more medals and an enormous breakfast.

Dismal and Dull go.

I think that fooled them.

Gloria And then there's Grizzelda …

Gilbert What about her?

Gloria She creeps about the palace being very quiet and thoughtful. It's weird and unnatural. We mustn't let on to her we've got problems.

Gilbert We mustn't let on to anyone we've got problems.

Dismal and Dull return with breakfast.

Gloria Have you checked it for things that might assassinate us?

Dismal Yes, your magnificence.

Gilbert So there are no little plastic toys in the cereal cunningly designed to stick in our throats and choke us to death?

Dull No, your magnificence.

Gloria And no capsules in the teapot which might release a deadly poisonous laughing gas that would make us laugh our heads horribly right off?

Dismal No, your magnificence.

Gloria Then you may serve breakfast.

Dull ***(coughs)*** Your magnificences, Mrs Dismal and I were wondering if you'd given any more thought to tracking down our Derek and Eric?

Gilbert How many more times? You know very well there is nothing at all unusual about children disappearing in this country. It's completely normal. What on earth makes you think your Derek and Eric are anything special?

Dismal ***(munching on a piece of toast that Gloria has given her to test)*** But your magnificence, you said you'd look in to our case.

Gloria Well, we fibbed, so what? No-one is the least bit interested in where your children ended up. Your Derek and Eric are of no importance or interest to anyone. No-one cares at all, so shut up about it.

A huge bag of mail crashes on to the table.

Dismal That'll be the post, your majesty.

Gilbert What's this? ***(He tears open an envelope)*** 'Dear Gilbert and Gloria Grimm, we want to know what happened to Derek Dismal and Eric Dull who disappeared many years ago …'

Gloria ***(reading another)*** 'We are worried about the way you have treated many such cases in the past and continue to do so …'

Gilbert ***(reading another)*** 'We believe you have illegally imprisoned Bobby Bunting, an innocent joke salesman, and ask you to free him immediately …

Gloria ***(reading another)*** 'PS. All the other letters on the table say the same thing …'

Gilbert ***(reading yet another)*** 'PPS. The world is watching you.'

Dull Anything the matter, your magnificence?

Gloria ***(after a pause)*** Absolutely not. Another joke cobbled together by cheerful ones with nothing better to do than make trouble.

Gilbert Not something to be taken seriously at all, is it, dear?

Gloria Not at all. ***(She suddenly loses her temper)*** *What a blinking nerve, eh? If I could get hold of one of those little scribblers who wrote these I'd bag them for the rest of their lives, what a blinking nerve!* ***(She jumps up and down on a letter.*** **Grizzelda** ***comes in.)***

Grizzelda What are you shouting about, Mum?

Gloria Nothing, dearest. Your father gets me wild sometimes.

Grizzelda What a lot of letters. Who are they from?

Gloria Oh, just the fan-mail for my latest album of patriotic songs. What would you like for breakfast?

Grizzelda Nothing thank you, Mum.

Gloria Grizzy, you're off your nosh. What's the matter?

Grizzelda I've been thinking.

Gloria Now you know your father doesn't like you doing that, don't you?

Grizzelda I want to ask you a question. What happens to ordinary folk after they've broken the law?

Gilbert I've told you: they're sent to prison.

Grizzelda And what happens then?

Gilbert They learn how to be a proper sensible person. They learn to stop finding us funny. And they learn that because me and your mother are the most high-minded and stern and unfunny people you could ever wish to meet …

Grizzelda So why do you watch funny films?

A nasty pause.

Gloria Why, Grizzelda, you know all funny films are absolutely banned completely. What can you mean?

Grizzelda I mean those funny films you watch in your private cinema at night when you think everyone else has gone to sleep and can't see.

Gilbert Have you been spying on us?

Gloria Those aren't funny films. No, no. They're important and weighty reports by the Head of the Armed Forces, the Chief of the Secret Police and – and the Minister for Bath Plugs

Grizzelda Oh, yes? And since when has the Chief of Secret Police and the Head of the Armed Forces been two brightly coloured animals who chase each other around all the time tripping each other up and when one of them wacks the other over the head with a saucepan you two laugh and laugh until the tears run down your face?

Gloria You have been spying on us.

Grizzelda So shouldn't you go to prison and learn how to be proper, sensible people?

Gilbert You're a spy! My own daughter is a spy! The next thing you know the whole fabric of our society will be breaking down.

The noise of a crowd is heard from offstage.

Crowd *(faintly)* Bunting! Bunting!

Gloria What's that?

Crowd *(louder)* Bunting! Bunting!

Dismal Looks like it's the whole fabric of your society breaking down, your magnificence.

The Grimms rush to the window and draw back the curtain.

Gloria It's a demonstration. Go to your room, Grizzelda. Enough of your accusations.

Grizzelda stomps off.

Gilbert What are they shouting?

Crowd *(louder)* Bunting! Bunting! We want Bunting!

Gloria What are we going to do?

A letter falls on to the table.

If I have one more letter from a whingeing do-gooder about some nobody who's disappeared I shall belt someone.

Gloria picks it up and tears it open.

'Attention of Gilbert and Gloria Grimm. Stop. Request permission to proceed with readjustment of Prisoner 25168 Bunting B. Stop. Love Doctor Bleach. This telegram top secret. Do not read out loud. Stop.

Gilbert Give that here ***(He snatches it. He whispers.)*** This is the answer to our prayers, Gloria. ***(Dismal and Dull strain to hear)***

Gloria Let's tell the doctor to start the treatment straightaway. If we can break Bunting it will show that crowd we can break anyone.

Gilbert And let's send the army in to break them up. We're surrounded by enemies. It's either us or them.

Dismal and Dull suddenly fall to the floor retching and spluttering.

There, what did I tell you? It's an assassination attempt. ***(He leans over them.)***

Dismal ***(taking the telegram from his pocket)*** Tell Eric ... ***(She pretends to die.)***

Dull Tell Derek ... ***(She pretends to die.)***

Gloria Here, good job we didn't have any jam, Gilbert. ***(They observe the Crowd outside.)***

Gloria Sometimes I wish the lot of them had one head then we could shove one big bag over it for good.

They go. Dismal and Dull jump up. Grizzelda returns.

Grizzelda Mrs Dismal and Mrs Dull, I've decided, we have to rescue Bobby Bunting. I'm sure the answer to what happened to Derek and Eric lies in that top secret prison where he's held. If we only knew where it was.

Dismal produces the telegram.

Dismal Look no further, Miss Grizzelda. I've got the telegram and it's got the address on it.

Dull Nice work, Dilys.

Grizzelda The stage is set for me to be a heroine. For I see now what a very bad and wrong little girl I have been. I see now how much poor ordinary folk like you have suffered because of my Mum and Dad. And most of all now I see, yes, I see how very much I love Bobby Bunting ...

Dismal I think I'm really going to be sick now Mrs Dull.

Grizzelda My plan is this: I break single-handed in to the top secret prison and rescue Bobby Bunting and you two help me smuggle him to safety back to his own country. What do you think, ladies, will you help?

Dull Sounds bound to completely fail and to end in all three of us meeting a sudden and very nasty death, miss.

Both We'll do it. ***(They all shake hands and grin.)***

Crowd We want Bunting! Bunting! Bunting!

7 THE CELL

The Book As this brave trio make their pact
Government thugs were in the act
Of silencing what the crowd
Were shouting for so long and loud
But Bunting cannot hear their cries
In the prison where he lies
Behind steel doors and walls of stone
In the darkness, all alone.

*Darkness. Outside Bunting's cell, **Soldier One** and **Two** stand on guard. **Bunting** is singing.*

Soldier 2 He doesn't seem very depressed yet does he? I don't think this treatment is working.

Soldier 1 Patience, Soldier One. This is a battle of wills. In the face of our grim determination he's bound to crack eventually. We've got all the time in the world, we have. We'll do whatever it takes.

Soldier 2 Will we, Soldier One? What does that mean? What are we going to do next?

Soldier 1 Calm down, Soldier Two. What's the matter with you?

Soldier 2 Well, I'm feeling very jumpy. I keep thinking something very nasty's about to happen. Or is happening. What's going on outside? Why was there no newspaper this morning?

Soldier 1 No newspaper: no news, Soldier Two. So nothing's happening. That means outside everything's just the same. Everyday, boring, normal.

Soldier 2 But I've heard the prisoners whispering, Soldier One.

Soldier 1 Don't listen to wild talk. Specially from comics.

Soldier 2 What if it's true what they say: that there are mobs on the street this morning? What if they are shouting for prisoners to be set free?

Soldier 1 But it's not true, Soldier Two. Out there, it's just a morning like any other. The radios chattering away, the telephones ring, the dogs yawn …

Soldier 2 … But what if they do send in the security forces?

Soldier 1 There's no need for violence. Not if everyone quietly gets on with their jobs …

Soldier 2 … if they'll do anything to stamp them out …

Bunting ***(off)*** Oi, what are you whispering?

Soldier 1 … if we all just try to keep calm …

Soldier 2 … *Who's going to get hurt?*

Soldier 1 *Listen, no one will get hurt if they do what they're told and don't ask questions. No one will get hurt because nothing is going on here, because nothing ever goes on here, because everything is always normal and boring. Alright?*

Soldier One has his cosh over Soldier Two's head. A Doctor comes in.

Doctor What's going on here, Soldier One?

Soldier 1 *Nothing, nothing at all, nothing* – hello, Doctor. I was just explaining to Soldier Two why no-one ever gets hurt here.

Doctor Whatever put that thought in your head? We only want to cure these poor fools. And now I have the go-ahead to use my experimental treatment on this especially bad case here, it will happen even quicker. Has Patient Bunting received his calming injection?

Soldier 2 Yes, Doctor.

Bunting There once was a serious young doctor
Who put all the comics behind locked doors
Not trying to cheat them
But trying to treat them
Though none of them understood what for

Doctor Hmm! Bring in the apparatus from the corridor, please

***Soldier One** and **Soldier Two** go off. **Doctor** turns on the single bare bulb in the cell. **Bunting** blinks.*

Bunting Doctor, Doctor. I keep thinking I'm in a madhouse.

Doctor Of course. So, we are going to set you free.

Bunting No, no, no, that was a joke. The punchline is, get to the back of the queue with all the other singing rabbits – you're what?

Doctor I said we are going to set you free.

Bunting Really?

Doctor Oh yes. It's time for you to be returned to the real world.

*The **Soldiers** bring on a large armchair and go off again.*

Make yourself comfortable, please.

Bunting *(sitting in the chair)* I knew you'd come round in the end. Been a losing battle hasn't it? Well you have been up against a professional. It was all just a matter of time. Well, it's been super chatting, an experience knowing you, but I won't keep you any longer. Got my suitcase, have you? Or do I pick it up at the door?

Doctor You have been in prison for a very, very long time.

Bunting Well, a month, yes …

Doctor A very dark and lonely prison.

Bunting Mmmm …

Doctor What we must do is to help you – readjust to the outside world. It won't take long. Your freedom is at hand.

***Soldiers** return with two trolleys on which are two black boxes with wires.*

Soldier 2 *(nervously)* What are these things, Doctor?

Doctor Nothing to be frightened of, Soldier Two. Only two ordinary household appliances. Turn it on, it's perfectly harmless.

***Soldier Two** turns on his box.*

Box And now State Radio news. Outside the palace of our glorious leaders this morning, a rabble of 600 hooligans demanded the release of the terrorist and foreign spy, Bobby Bunting who …

Soldier 2 So it is true …

Bunting Is it? Do they mean me? Do they really?

Doctor Oh yes. Switch off.

***Soldier Two** turns the box off.*

Bunting *(joyful)* Well, I knew I wouldn't be forgotten but I never expected such a huge display of public support. Isn't that kind? No, isn't it? They cared, they cared enough to come out on the streets for me and now I'm going free. I'm over the moon, I really am. I'm going to throw such a party for them all, it'll be massive and …

Soldier 1 Shall I belt him one, Doctor?

Doctor No no, none of that crude stuff. We are civilised. We are scientific. And we *care.* Gentlemen, gag the patient, please.

***Soldiers** tie Bunting down in the armchair and gag him.*

Now, as we have all seen, the patient continues to show that he has a topsy-turvy view of himself as an innocent victim not a guilty criminal. Gentlemen, before your very eyes I shall *change his point of view*. Connect Box A to the patient's eyes, Soldier Two.

***Soldier One** puts something resembling a pair of binoculars over Bunting's eyes.*

Connect Box B to the patient's ears.

***Soldier Two** puts something resembling a pair of headphones over Bunting's ears.*

Look on in wonder, gentlemen, as I cure this so-called incurable, as I transform this funny little fellow by showing him his real place in the world. The real world of everyday misery and evil. Turn on your box, Soldier One

***Soldier One** turns it on.*

Doctor *(to Bunting)* Now your eyes are slowly filling with images, as if you were watching today's news with the sound turned down. You can see the demonstration today. You see the banners and marching feet moving in slow motion, the chanting mouths in the faces of the crowd opening and shutting. Now you see our security forces moving in. The coshes are cracking down on to those faces, crack, smack. And you think this is an outrage, this must be stopped, the world will not let it happen etcetera. Of course you do. Now turn on your box too, Soldier Two.

***Soldier Two** turns it on.*

Doctor Now a noise is beginning to trickle into your ears as you see this violence go on. It is a sound very familiar to you. You will remember it from your own cheerful country. It is the laughter of a happy audience. *(to Soldiers)* Remember, gentlemen, the patient has spent his whole life making people laugh away their troubles. But with such terrible violence right in front of your nose, doesn't it sound horrible, shameful, now? Quick, switch over, he thinks. Switch over, gentlemen. What's on the other side?

Soldiers switch over.

Doctor Look it's the faces of that happy audience. They're smiling, they're laughing, they're cheering. But all you can hear is sound of those demonstrators. Their pain, their suffering and the name they were shouting as the army broke them up. Bunting! Bunting! Bunting! Not cheering for you but cries against you. You made them suffer. You made them laugh. All of it: your fault. You feel guilty twice over, more, you feel guilty of everything. Ah, but then that's the real world for you. What can you do? You've got to laugh haven't you? Laugh a little 'oh-well' laugh, a little 'that's the real world' laugh.

(to the Soldiers) Gentlemen, the cure will be complete when the patient laughs this laugh. It will be his last laugh. A little gurgle of despair and all hope goes down the plug-hole. Then he will enter the real world. And he will be free.

Bunting struggles.

Soldier 2 ***(whispers to Soldier One)*** Soldier One, didn't they do something like this to us when we were children? I'm so confused, do you think that's why? Is that why I'm confused?

Soldier 1 There's nothing confused about this. It's a miracle of modern technology.

Bunting struggles, mumbles 'Help'.

Soldier 2 No. Stop it.

Doctor Be quiet, Soldier Two. Come on 25168, just one last laugh …

Soldier 2 Won't do it …

A rope appears above their heads.

Grizzelda ***(off)*** Help! Someone better jolly well catch me.

Grizzelda falls directly on to the Doctor. They crash to the ground. Soldier Two pulls out the wires in his machine and the deafening sound of canned laughter fills the stage. Bunting holds his ears. Soldier Two starts to cry. Grizzelda and the Doctor struggle.

Doctor Grizzelda? How did you get in here, the most closely guarded prison in the country? Surrounded as it is by miles of walls, trenches and trip wires and patrolled by searchlights, huge dogs and grim sentries …

Grizzelda Tiny hurdles to a true heroine who will stop at nothing to see justice done, Doctor. And, besides, you left the back door open. Release Bobby Bunting. I have orders from the top to set him free.

Doctor Nonsense. I have had orders from the top to complete his treatment at all costs.

Grizzelda And I have a gun, so there. Untie him. Now keep back. ***(shouts off)*** Dismal and Dull, open wide the gates and let all go free! ***(Grizzelda helps Bunting off.)***

Doctor Get after them ***(Soldiers run off. Doctor sighs)*** Oh well. I nearly performed a miracle. ***(Doctor goes to turn off the lights and is suddenly caught in a spotlight.)***

Gloria ***(off)*** You failed, Doctor. You left the back door open.

Doctor Yes …

Gilbert ***(off)*** If you want to last, you'll learn to shut all the doors, close all the windows. Turn off all the lights …

Gloria ***(off)*** Finish what you start. Says so in the manual.

Doctor Yes, but …

The light snaps off.

8 THE CELL

The Book Dull and Dismal lay in wait
By the open prison gate
Not alone in their need to know
The fates of those lost long ago
But escape was now the thought of all
Not the crime behind the wall
Fearing that, with no repentance
The Grimms will pass the final sentence
Those who once had made a stand
Run in terror across the land
All hopes crumbling in disorder
Tumbling headlong for the border

The page turns.

The border as in Scene 1. The sign is hanging off its post. Bunting and Grizzelda run on.

Grizzelda There, you just have to step across and you're free. ***(Pause. Bunting hesitates.)*** What's your country like?

Bunting My country? It's very different from here. There are no laws against laughter. No-one's punished for wanting to be happy.

Grizzelda No wonder everyone's trying to get here then.

Bunting Everyone there is very cheerful all the time. The shops are very colourful. Every other shop is a sweet shop. In my country we eat a lot of sweets.

Grizzelda Don't their teeth go all black and fall out?

Bunting Oh, yes. But then we buy a much better pair of false ones – big, and white and gleaming. Put in by a very jolly dentist. No one has to worry about teeth. They can just laugh about teeth. They shout at each other across the street: 'Have you heard the latest teeth joke'?. 'Yes, it's a killer isn't it'? And they roar and bark and scream with laughter as they shove bag after bag of sweets into their big white smiles …

Grizzelda Sounds fab.

Bunting Somehow, right now, I'm not so sure.

Grizzelda Well, don't go all serious on me.

Bunting Yes, that's what the cheerful policemen say back home.

Grizzelda Oh, listen, I've decided. I'm coming with you. How can I go back home now? I'm so happy. Oh Bobby, isn't it as plain as the lovely little nose on my fabulous face that I love you ***(She flings open her arms.)*** Will you marry me? ***(A gunshot)*** Crikey.

Soldier Two runs on.

Soldier 1 ***(off)*** Shoot, Soldier Two.

Bunting and Grizzelda run off. Soldier One runs on.

Soldier 1 Why didn't you shoot? We're supposed to shoot on sight any traitors.

Soldier 2 Why?

Soldier 1 What do you mean 'Why'? Because those are our orders and we obey orders.

Soldier 2 Why?

Soldier 1 Because we're soldiers.

Soldier 2 Why?

Soldier 1 Because we were born soldiers. So get soldiering.

Soldier 2 No, Soldier One. I've come to a decision. I don't want to actually be a soldier anymore, actually.

Soldier 1 ***(outraged)*** Don't want to be a soldier?!

Soldier 2 No. I mean, I don't know how I ended up a soldier in the first place. Did I want to threaten, bully, hurt and kill people? Did I want people to look at me and think 'What a very nasty young man you are'? Is that job satisfaction? Is it? Well, from now on, when people look at me I want them to *love* me. ***(A dreamy smile drifts across his face.)*** I want to be a popular entertainer. A cabaret performer. ***(ecstatic)*** Or even, yes, why not, a game-show host?

Soldier 1 ***(points his gun)*** That's enough, Soldier Two, I'm going to shoot you.

Soldier 2 laughs.

Soldier 2 But we're friends, Soldier One.

Soldier 1 ***(astonished)*** Friends? Whatever gave you that idea? You've never been anything but another soldier to me. And now you've laughed you're nothing at all.

Soldier 2 No, Soldier One, don't you remember a long time ago before – before … don't you remember us playing in a park and we were friends. You must remember.

Soldier 1 ***(his finger on the trigger)*** No.

Soldier 2 Please don't shoot me, Soldier One. Please. Don't be silly. ***(yells)*** I want my mum.

Dismal and Dull appear.

Dismal and **Dull** *Who wants a mother?*

Soldier 1 Who are you?

Dismal Who are you?

Soldier 1 We're two soldiers who have orders to shoot on sight any suspected traitors.

Dull Oh but everyone was having such an exciting time for a change.

Dismal Yes, everything was so free and different.

Soldier 1 ***(storms up to them)*** Listen, what is getting into everyone?

Why does everyone want things to be different? I don't. If everything was different, nobody would know who they were would they?

Dull ***(looking at Soldier One closely)*** But who are you?

Dismal ***(looking at Soldier Two)*** And who are you?

Soldier 1 I'm Soldier One who's a soldier and this is Soldier Two, who's a …

Soldier 2 Game show host …

Soldier 1 Another soldier …

Dismal But weren't you given names by your mums?

Soldier 1 We never had mums. Right, Soldier Two, it's make your mind up time. Do you want to be a live, unpopular soldier or a dead popular entertainer?

Soldier 2 ***(aside)*** Strange how being faced with your own death makes being popular a bit irrelevant.

He points his rifle at Dismal and Dull.

Dismal ***(to Soldier One)*** So you haven't got a birthmark in the shape of a mole on your right shoulder-blade then?

Dull ***(to Soldier 2)*** And you haven't got a tattoo of a large grapefruit on your left thigh, then?

Soldier 1 and **2** Yes … mother?

Soldier 1 ***(aside)*** Funny how being faced by your own mother can suddenly change your political opinions.

He goes to embrace Dismal. Soldier Two embraces Dull. Grizzelda and Bunting come back.

Grizzelda Hold it there.

Dull Don't shoot …

Dismal Not now we've found happiness and each other …

Grizzelda Then, we must cross the border now. Let's all go, hand in hand, joyfully to freedom …

They all hold hands. A tank appears, on it are Gloria and Gilbert.

Gilbert Make another move and we'll blow you all into tiny bits of tiny bits.

They stop.

Gloria Turn, turn again, oh, you wicked ones. Face the final sentence of the Grimms. You broke our law. You take our punishment. And our punishment is death.

Bunting Death? You can't do that.

Gilbert Oh yes we can.

Bunting But for the sake of sanity …

Gloria *(very cool)* Sanity? Sanity? Well, we weren't the ones finding all this funny.

Gilbert Well, you have had your fun and now it's over.

Gloria Time to say 'goodbye' everyone.

Gilbert Goodbye.

The barrel of the tank rises.

Gloria and Gilbert Five, four, three, two, one …

Grizzelda steps out.

Grizzelda Hold on. Just hold on. What's going on? Who wrote this? It can't end like this, can it? ***(She snatches up the Book.)*** Look, it says 'The Last Laugh – a fairy tale'. Fairy tales have never, will never end with ***(She reads …)*** 'And so it was that everyone was blown away by a tank …' I noticed the last five minutes getting far too serious and I wasn't going to say anything but this was the last straw. This story-line has got far too oppressive.

She tears out the last page of the Book.

Now we're going to have a proper fairy tale ending. A proper, unbelievably nice ending. ***(She shouts offstage)*** My unbelievably nice costume please ***(A fairy costume is thrown on, she struggles into it.)*** … And the wand? Who's got my wand? ***(A tinsel wand is thrown on. She picks it up.)*** So, here it is. The right ending.

The wand is waved.

Gloria and **Gilbert** Five, four, three, two, one …

Gloria *(to Gilbert)* Shall we tell them?

Gilbert *(to Gloria)* Go on then, let's.

Gloria and **Gilbert** *(bellow joyously)* *Had you fooled!*

All laugh with mixed surprise and relief.

Gloria and **Gilbert** *Had you going!*

Gilbert Twenty five years of oppressive dictatorship.

Gloria And it was all really one big, glorious practical *joke*.

Gloria and **Gilbert** And you *fell for it!*

Dull Well I never …

Gloria and **Gilbert** *Had you fooled! Had you going!*

Grizzelda *(to the audience)* And so it was that everything turned out nice like it should. Mothers were reunited with sons, daughters with fathers. Gilbert and Gloria became the kindly old couple they always had been really. ***(Gilbert gets out a pipe, Gloria some knitting)*** Mrs Dismal and Mrs Dull with their sons Derek and Eric opened the first ever sweet shop in this land which had once been so sad and dreary.

A deluge of confetti, bunting, balloons and tickertape begins to fall. Loud triumphal music and wedding bells.

Everyone came to see me and Bobby Bunting get married and as the guards lined the streets everyone agreed how lovely I was and everyone forgot all the depressing things and everyone was happy and everyone was free …

All are waving except Bunting who seems to be trying to say something. The light fades as they disappear under the celebration …

EPILOGUE: THE CELL

Bunting sits in the armchair under the single bulb. He holds the book with its ripped last page.

Bunting So with a tantrum and some magic
Grizzelda stopped it turning tragic
And if her ending seemed to you
Too sweet and neat to be true,
If her smile had a steely look
To shut up the tales of this book:
The last laugh of its story must be yours
To reach beyond a prison's doors.
The last page torn, who can mend it?
Can you begin to really end it?

The End

ACTIVITIES

TALKING POINTS

1 Look at the facts shown opposite. They are taken from recent leaflets published by Amnesty International and books on human rights. Which of these issues do you think are touched upon in ***The Last Laugh***?

2 The play starts in an empty cell lit by a single light bulb.

- Work in a small group. Sketch a picture of such a cell. Around the outside of your picture jot down words and phrases that come to mind when you think of such a place.
  In the cell we see a large open book and hear a voice reading its first page.
- Look at your picture again and have one of your group read the first page aloud as if it is from a children's story.
- Talk about the effect Ben Payne is trying to achieve by starting his play in this way.

3 What do you imagine the country ruled by the Grimms is like? What sort of buildings do you imagine? What are the people like?

- In pairs, imagine that you are on an aeroplane returning from a visit to the country as it is when the play starts. Talk about the things you saw there and the atmosphere you experienced.
- Now talk about where you think the images in your head actually came from.

4 Although ***The Last Laugh*** is mainly a comedy, do you think that the final impression an audience is left with is a happy one?

- Read through Scene 7 again and pick out at least three lines or incidents that seem designed to 'freeze the smiles on the audiences' faces'.
- Talk about how Ben Payne changes the tone of the play towards the end.

ABUSES OF HUMAN RIGHTS?

- People can be imprisoned without charge or trial in over 50 countries. Sometimes for years. In Burma, one girl was just a year old when she was imprisoned with her mother. She stayed there for 31 years.
- More than 60 countries are known to use torture when interrogating suspects. This treatment isn't just for adults. Children as young as 12 are known to have been tortured in some countries.
- 'Prisoners of conscience' are currently being held in over 70 countries. In some cases they are accused simply of saying something which their government didn't like.
- More than 90 countries still have the death penalty. This is not always for murder or rape, but often for 'political offences'.
- In 1992 in the USA, 36 people were sentenced to death for crimes they committed when they were still under 18 years of age.
- Thousands of children are known to have 'disappeared' in Argentina prior to 1982 when a new leader came to power. In Guatemala children forced to sleep rough on the streets are 'cleaned up' at night by 'Death Squads' thcught to consist mainly of police and army members.
- Kurds living in the mountains between Iraq and Turkey were bombed and gassed by both countries during the 1980s.
- Thousands of Barzani tribespeople, including 300 children between 8 and 17 years of age, were arrested by Iraq in the early 1980s. Nothing has been heard of them since.
- Prior to December 1989, the Romanian Ministry of Internal Affairs kept records on typewriter production and the distribution of ink and type ribbons. To buy a typewriter, individuals had to apply to the local military.
- Between 1987 and 1990, an estimated 40,000 people 'disappeared' in Sri Lanka.

Countries such as Britain and the USA have often been called 'the Free World'. But while there may not be such obvious abuses of human rights in those countries, Governments nevertheless decide what people are allowed to know. For example:

- In 1983 Sarah Tisdale, a young civil servant, told the newspapers that cruise missiles were to be brought into Britain in secret. She was imprisoned for six months.
- Also in 1983, Clive Ponting revealed that the British government had not told the whole truth about the sinking of the Argentine battleship *Belgrano* in which over 300 sailors died.
- In 1985 the British Government banned a book called *Spycatcher*. The book gave details of how British agents worked and even revealed how plans had been made to get rid of 1970s Labour Prime Minister Harold Wilson.
- In 1988 members of the Irish political party Sinn Fein were banned from speaking on radio or television because of their association with the IRA.

5 Look through the examples of human rights cases again. Which 'human rights' do you think are being 'abused'? Talk about these questions:

- Do you think a Government should have to ban the publication of things or censor what people say?
- What sort of things do you think it is right to ban or censor?
- What do you think would be a fair punishment for breaking such a ban?
- Find out what things are banned and censored in this country. Do you think these laws abuse human rights or protect them?

WRITE

6 When we look back to Scene One we get a taste of some of the odd laws that have been imposed by the Grimms. For example:

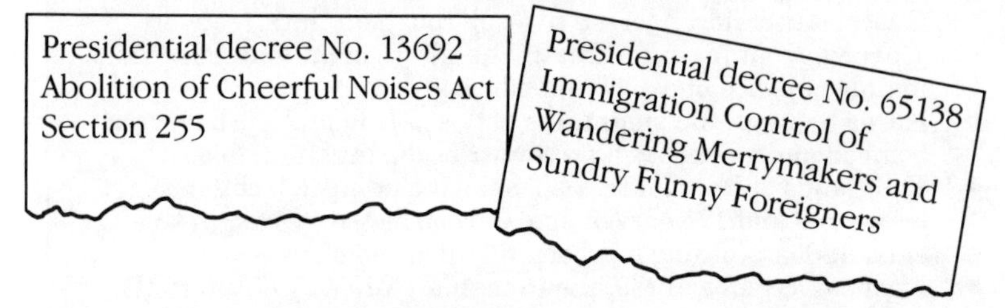

- Make up some other laws which you think might exist in the land.
- Choose one of them and write the details of what the law actually involves. Try to use appropriately 'official' language.

7 On page 9 Gloria Grimm displays a *Wanted* poster for Bobby Bunting. Reproduce the poster. Take care to use a style of drawing and language that fits this play.

8 Gloria Grimm seems fond of singing patriotic songs about the wonderful things she and Gilbert have done for their people. Write the lyrics of another song for her.

9 Look back at the facts overleaf and think about the overall effect of ***The Last Laugh***. How do things like this make you feel? Write down your response in the form of a poem. Remember that poems are just ideas in words; they don't *have* to rhyme. In fact, as you will see below, rhymes can sometimes get in the way of expressing what you really feel and mean!

10 Re-read the words from the Book on page 8.

- What do you notice about the way this speech rhymes? Does this type of rhyme remind you of other things you have read? Why do you think Ben Payne has used this kind of 'rhyme scheme'?
- Read the speech aloud. Try and emphasise the rhythm by 'bouncing' along each line. Talk again about what this sort of rhythm reminds you of.
- Sometimes Ben has to write a line in an odd way just to get the rhyme in. For example:

  His cheek must be denounced aloud
  From their balcony to the crowd.

  Look at the other pages from the Book and pick out three more examples of where the usual way of saying something is twisted just to get a rhyme.

11 This type of writing is sometimes called 'doggerel verse'; in it, the emphasis is on rhyme and rhythm. In ***The Last Laugh***, this reminds us of how artificial the whole story is (though there is, of course, a serious point lurking just below the surface).

Now read this example of verse from the *Poetic Gems* of William McGonagall, a devout monarchist and nationalist who wrote many poems in praise of famous people. He was perhaps the greatest writer of doggerel verse that ever lived (though he probably never realised it and no-one had the heart to tell him!)

Attempted Assassination of the Queen

God prosper long our noble Queen,
And long may she reign!
Maclean he tried to shoot her,
But it was all in vain.

For God He turned the ball aside
Maclean aimed at her head;
And he felt very angry
Because he didn't shoot her dead.

...

Maclean must be a madman,
which is obvious to be seen,
Or else he wouldn't have tried to shoot
Our most beloved Queen.

Victoria is a good Queen,
Which all her subjects know,
And for that God has protected her
From all her deadly foes.

...

Long may she be spared to roam
Among the bonnie Highland floral,
And spend many a happy day
In the palace of Balmoral.

Because she is very kind
To the old women there,
And allows them bread, tea, and sugar,
And each one to get a share.

...

I hope God will protect her
By night and by day,
At home and abroad
When she's far away.

May He be as a hedge around her,
As He's been all along,
And let her live and die in peace
Is the end of my song.

- Try reading the poem aloud. McGonagall wrote it to be taken seriously but is that possible? Why is there a difference between the response he wants to produce and the response he actually gets? What stops us from taking it seriously?
- Pick a serious event which has recently been in the news and write a short verse about it. It matters not a jot how you twist the lines, so long as you're sure your poem rhymes.

12 This type of rhyming and strong rhythm actually has a powerful modern cousin in the form of rap.

- Look at the speech on page 8 and in small groups rehearse it as a rap. Does it become more powerful when performed in this way? If so, how do you explain that?
- Try performing the *Attempted Assassination of the Queen* or your own piece of doggerel verse as a rap. Do they suddenly acquire a new, punchy meaning? How? Why?

DRAMA

13 Sometimes people are punished just for what they're thinking. But how do you prove what someone might be thinking? Improvise one of the following scenes.

- A group of you are standing at the bus stop when someone else walks by. One member of the group follows the passer-by with his/her eyes. Another group member starts the improvisation with the line: 'You fancy him/her don't you'?
- A dangerously funny joke has come into the hands of the secret police. As one of their top agents, it is your job to find people who think that this joke is funny. You have already gathered in some suspects and intend to find out who the gigglers are (but remember that laughing yourself will lose you your job).

14 Try playing these word games.

- In pairs, play the *Yes/No* game. That is, one person asks a series of questions to which the other must make a reply but is not allowed to say either *Yes* or *No*. As soon as either of these words is uttered the person is out and you must change over.

How able were you to stay aware of what you were actually saying in this game?

- In pairs, both of you should start a conversation at exactly the same time. The aim is to talk your partner into silence. One way would be to simply shout louder, but see if you can find more subtle ways of simply insisting that you are heard.

As a group, talk about the successful methods which were discovered.

- In small groups start a conversation but every word which would normally begin with the letter 'b' must become 'banana'. So, a sentence might run, 'It was a banana sunny day so my younger banana and I went down to the banana lake in the park'. If anybody trips up they are given a slip of paper. Keep the conversation going for five minutes, trying to catch other people in your group out. The winner is the person with least slips.

Talk about how the relationships in this conversation were affected by the rules of the game.

15 Work as a whole class on this role play:

Imagine that there is a country where believing in Father Christmas has been banned (this was actually the case in Albania). Some people however continue to believe. Your teacher will give you a card. A small number of them will say 'Happy Christmas, luv Santa' – if you get one of these you are a secret believer and it is your job to find who else in the group you can trust. A few cards will say 'Ba Humbug'! – you are secret police whose job it is to find the believers and arrest them. If you have a blank card you're just an ordinary person – will you betray those you know to believe?

Keep the role play going for at least ten minutes. At a given signal, the secret police must make their arrests. If the believers are able to gather in to groups of three or more they will be saved from arrest.

Discuss how you felt about each other during the role play. How did you feel about the situation you were in?

What would be an appropriate punishment for those who were arrested for believing in Father Christmas?

PLAYING THE CHARACTERS

A FAIRY TALE?

1 Ben Payne has sub-titled his play *A Fairy Tale*.

- Write a paragraph which explains how the story is like a fairy tale.
- Complete the chart below which shows how some of the characters in ***The Last Laugh*** could be compared with typical fairy tale characters. You will probably be able to find better examples than the ones given here. Put as many characters from the play as you can into the chart.

Fairy Tale Character	Example	Last Laugh Character	Reason for likeness
Giant	in Jack & the Beanstalk	Gilbert	Stupid, lazy, relies on force
Queen	of Hearts in Alice in Wonderland	Gloria	Bossy. Vain. Always shouting things like ...
Princess			
		Bobby Bunting	

- Compare your chart with at least three other people and talk about the different ideas you have had.
- Now jot down five things that are said or done in the play which would remind an audience that they are not watching the usual kind of fairy tale. For example, Gloria and Gilbert threatening people with a tank.

2 Most of the characters in ***The Last Laugh*** are *two dimensional.* Like characters in fairytales they are what they seem. Unlike people in real life, they have no hidden elements to their personality. Their function in the play isn't to help us see them as individuals, but to help us see what the situation has done to people generally.

- In pairs, read and compare the conversation between Soldier One and Soldier Two in Scene 1 (pages 2–3) with the conversation Dull and Dismal have in Scene 3 (pages 14–15). What do these scenes tell you about the effect life in this country has had on them?
- Choose one of these scenes to work on in more depth. Is it possible to play the scene so that an audience would find the situation laughable but still feel sorry for the characters? Rehearse the scene and jot down your ideas on how the characters should be costumed and how they should speak and move.
- If there was a scene in the play which featured Mr Left and Mr Right, where do you think it should be and what sort of conversation would they have?

Between 1966 and 1986, the Philipines were ruled by President Marcos and his wife Imelda. The couple ruled with an iron fist, assassinating their political opponents and simply taking billions of dollars of the country's wealth for themselves. Imelda took delight in writing and singing songs about how great their leadership was.

Until 21 December 1989, Romania was ruled by Nicolae and Elena Ceausescu. On that day he stood on a balcony overlooking the main square in the capital, Bucharest. There had been some trouble in another town, so a rally had been organised by the security forces to show loyalty to him – but things didn't go as planned as this report by BBC reporter John Simpson shows: *Ceausescu began talking. Each time he paused there was more clapping in unison. He waved back, in a way that may have been intended to be modest but merely looked imperious. He was still thanking the Bucharest Party Committee for organising the rally when something altogether new happened, something Ceausescu had never heard in his life before. Part of the crowd was booing him. It began as a low groan, but quickly grew louder and higher. Over and above the groaning was another, sharper sound. People were whistling as well.*

It was a total surprise ... At last the words faded away altogether, and he stopped. His mouth was a little open. It was a laughable and shocking moment: a tyrant coming face to face with the hatred of his people, Macbeth watching the wood begin to move ... Elena Ceausescu's thin, harsh voice was picked up on the microphone:

'Stay calm, please.'

The Ceausescus fled but were quickly arrested, tried and executed. Their private apartments were believed to be full of gold. In fact, *'The carpets were thin and stained. The rooms dark and narrow ... There was a tacky feel to everything. The dining table had an imitation gold call-button to summon the servants, but the electrical cord was attached to the leg of the table with adhesive tape ... Their apartment was furnished from gifts, as though from a vast international wedding-list. Everything had a label ... Near his bed stood a toy tank. It had no label. It may have been the only thing Ceausescu had bought himself.'*

Eventually they were forced to flee the country. When the palace was taken over, it was found that Imelda Marcos had a bizzare collection of hundreds of pairs of shoes – presumably all bought with the money she was accused of having stolen from the people.

'I WOULD ALSO LIKE ANOTHER THREE THOUSAND TWO HUNDRED AND FIFTY PAIRS OF SLIPPERS TO BE TAKEN INTO CONSIDERATION'

3 ***The Last Laugh*** isn't about either the Marcos family or the Ceauscescus but about people who use their power for their own benefit. Sometimes people who behave like this are called tyrants or despots. When these people are rulers of countries it can be quite obvious how they are abusing their power. But perhaps other people have 'despotic tendencies' also. Perhaps when you have been asked to look after younger children you've experienced a feeling of power over them.

- Pay attention to current news items about people who have abused their power. Share your findings in class. Are some actions worse than others or is one abuse of power as bad as any other?

4 The photograph shows a scene from a famous French play called *Ubu Roi*. The play is a crazy kind of re-telling of the story of Macbeth. Ubu and his wife are coarse, gluttonous and childishly violent; more like Punch and Judy in fact than a King and Queen. Nevertheless, they take over as rulers after having the old king killed. Originally the play was written to be performed by puppets. When it was first performed by actors in 1896, its language and style literally caused a riot.

- In what way do you think the costumes and make up shown here would also suit Gilbert and Gloria in ***The Last Laugh***?
- Re-read Scene 2 from page 8 to Gilbert's line *That's enough, thanks* on page 10. Work in small groups to either act this scene out in a style suggested by the photograph or try out the scene using simple hand puppets.

5 Despots are often mocked by comedians. Recent programmes like *Spitting Image* delight in making fun of those people who seem to have gone 'power crazy'. Back in 1940 Charlie Chaplin made a film called *The Great Dictator* which made Hitler look ridiculous. Do you think it is a good thing to make fun of powerful people? Or do you think that people who abuse their power should be treated seriously? How do you feel people who are currently in the news for abusing their power should be treated?

DOCTOR BLEACH

6 *You don't want people to face up to real life. And what is real life but a very unhappy business*

In Scene 5, Bobby Bunting and the other prisoners meet Doctor Bleach, a person dedicated to making comedians and clowns face up to real life.

- Work in groups of three on the scene between Bleach and Bunting. One of you will direct the scene making it as funny as possible with Doctor Bleach being played as a comical, 'two-dimensional' mad scientist. Start from Bleach's line on page 32.
  This morning's lecture is entitled …
  and go on until:
  Forward, friends, to the real world!
- Swap roles and work through the scene again. This time, try to change the tone of the scene. Bunting should be played as someone who is always desperately trying to make a joke. Bleach should be played perfectly seriously as though the condition of the prisoners genuinely worries him or her. Compare the two scenes. Which do you think would have the most appropriate effect on an audience? Why?

7 Who is really the most frightening: madmen who are obviously mad, or people who give calm and reasonable arguments for mad actions? Re-read Doctor Bleach's speech on pages 43–44.

- Imagine that you are writing a report for Amnesty International. Use your own words to describe Doctor Bleach's method of torturing the prisoners.
- How could you play this scene so that it worries an audience rather than makes them laugh? Perhaps the key is in an earlier line when Doctor Bleach says:
  We are civilised. We are scientific. And we care. p. 43.

BOBBY BUNTING

8 What should Bobby Bunting look like? Should he wear a suit like a 'typical' travelling salesman, or should he be dressed as some kind of clown? Perhaps he should be a mixture of both.

- Design a costume for Bobby Bunting which will make him stand out from the other inhabitants of the country.

9 Do you like jokes or are there some jokes which you really don't find funny at all? How about the jokers themselves? Are they always popular or can they sometimes annoy you because they turn everything into a joke. Which of the jokers pictured opposite do you like? Why?

- Write a short paragraph saying why you like your favourite comedian.
- Now write a paragraph to explain why you dislike a particular comedian.

10 Read pages 48–50 again (from Gilbert's and Gloria's entrance on a tank to the end of Scene 8).

- Do you think this is a good ending? Perhaps you found it frustrating. How is it appropriate for this play?
- In groups, rehearse this extract. What should Bunting be doing during this scene?

11 The play ends with Bobby Bunting sitting in the cell holding the book.

- Jot down the ways in which Bunting's character seems to have changed. How would you show this in a performance?
- Set the scene up and experiment with different ways of playing Bunting's lines. What different effects do you get?
- what has made him change? What do you think he has realised at the end of the play?

12 Imagine that Bobby Bunting goes back to work in his own country but his heart just isn't in the job anymore. He is called to the head office of the Acme Joke Co. to explain why his sales have dropped so much. Devise a scene which shows what happens on his visit.

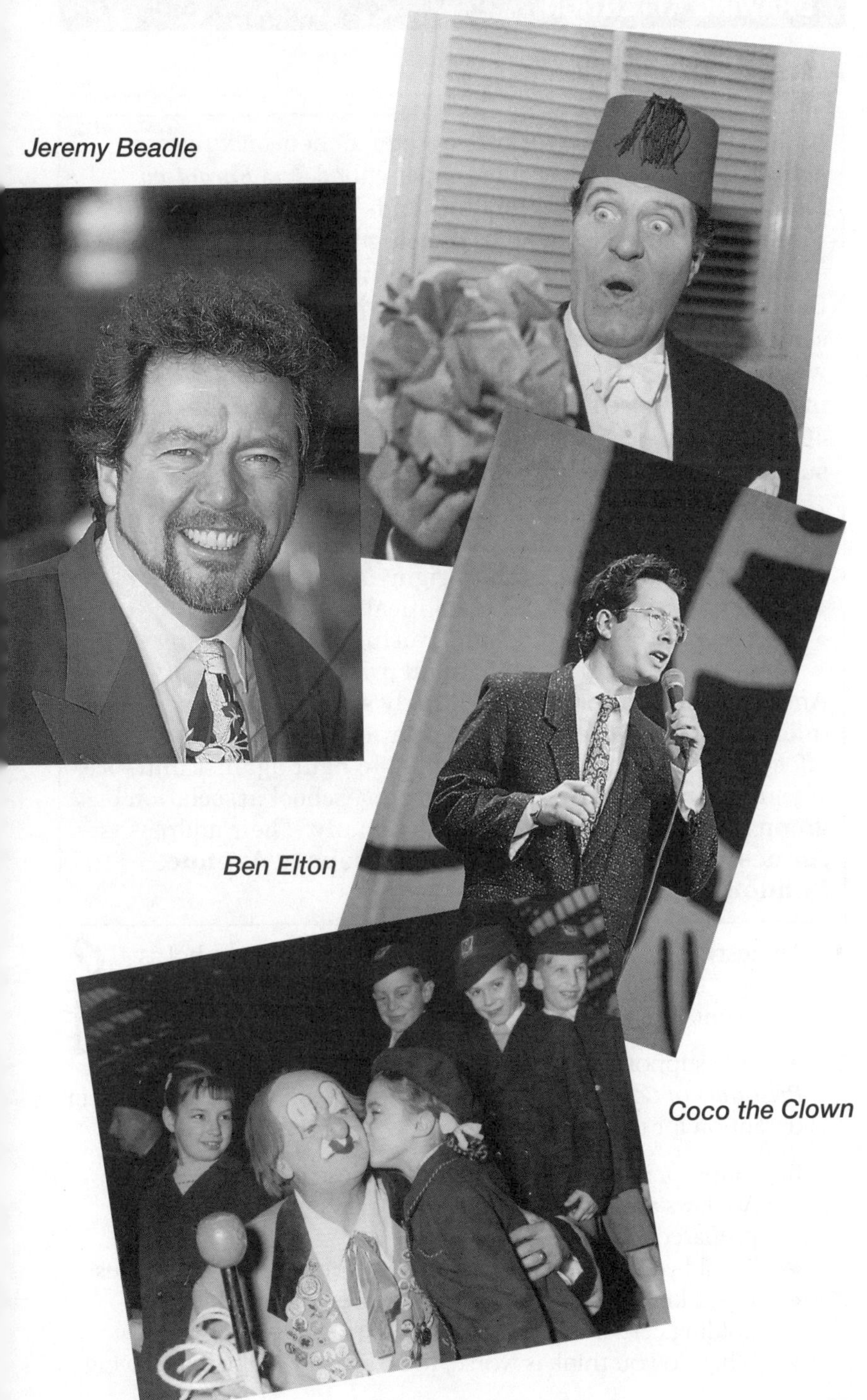

Tommy Cooper

Jeremy Beadle

Ben Elton

Coco the Clown

AMNESTY INTERNATIONAL

In 1961, a British lawyer called Peter Benenson wrote an article for The Observer newspaper called *The Forgotten Prisoners.* It was about the thousands of men and women throughout the world who were being held prisoner because of their political or religious views. Within a week, Peter Benenson had received 1000 offers of help to try and do something to protect human rights; Amnesty International was born. Since 1961 Amnesty International has investigated more than 43,500 cases of human rights abuse. 40,500 of those cases have been closed. In the eyes of its supporters, there is still a need to seek:

- The release of those men, women and children who are being held in 70 countries around the world for their beliefs, colour, sex, ethnic origin, language or religion.
- The fair and early trial of political prisoners.
- An end to the death penalty, torture and degrading treatment or punishment of all prisoners.

Amnesty International will willingly send out further information about how the organisation works and how effective campaigns can be mounted to fight against injustice. If you are interested you should form a school association or group rather than sending off individually. Their address is: **Amnesty International, 99–119 Rosebery Avenue, London EC1R 4RE**

1 Amnesty International has adopted this powerful symbol as its logo. Look at it carefully and discuss how you think it represents their aims as an organisation.

2 An early supporter of Amnesty International coined the term *Prisoners of Conscience* for those people who were being held in detention for their beliefs.

In groups, or as a whole class, discuss these questions:

- Are laws always right? What sort of laws would you be prepared to break?
- Would you go to prison for any of your beliefs? Which ones?
- If you knew that you could be tortured or even killed for holding certain beliefs, would you change yours?
- What do you think is worse, to be actually guilty of believing

something which is not allowed, or to say you don't believe something when really you do?
You may have disagreed strongly with each other in this discussion. The key question for you to think about is, what should happen to those people you disagree with?

- Write a poem which captures your feelings when you believe in something strongly yet others disagree with you.

3 Many of the people Amnesty International fight for are not guilty of any crime other than criticising their government in some way. However, Amnesty believes that torture and the death penalty are always wrong, no matter what the case. As a whole class, work through this exercise to explore the dilemmas which might be involved with this belief:

- Imagine that a woman has confessed to planting a bomb but is arrested before it goes off. She refuses to tell the authorities where it is planted.
  Three volunteers improvise a scene between the bomber, a prosecutor from the government who thinks that the information must be extracted from her, and a lawyer who is opposed to the use of torture.
- Imagine that the bomb goes off. Many people are killed. Improvise the scene in which the prosecution and defence lawyers argue what should happen to the bomber. What reasons does the bomber give to explain her action?
- Imagine that, after some kind of sentence is passed on the woman, it is discovered that she didn't plant the bomb at all; her 'confession' had been extracted through torture.
  Improvise the scene between the two lawyers when they next meet.
- Imagine that the woman is released from prison but not before she has been tortured.
  Improvise the scene when she meets the man who tortured her.
  Write a story or devise a scene in which someone has an opportunity to take revenge for something done to them. Do they take it? If not, what stops them?

4 *'We believe you have illegally imprisoned Bobby Bunting, an innocent joke salesman, and ask you to free him immediately'*

One of Amnesty's most successful methods of working is to simply send letters to Governments who are holding prisoners of conscience. Amnesty will give details of exactly who the letters should be sent to and even how to word the letters. This is what a union leader from the Dominican Republic told Amnesty officials after he was released:

> When the first 200 letters came, the guards gave me my clothes. The next 200 letters came and the prison officers came to see me. When the next pile of letters arrived the director got in touch with his superior. The letters kept coming, 3,000 of them, and the President called the prison and told them to let me go. After I was released the President called me to his office. He said: How is it a trade union leader like you has so many friends all over the world? He showed me an enormous box of letters he had received and when we parted he gave them to me.

- What do you know about Amnesty International? As a whole class, talk about other cases you think they have been involved with.
  - Amnesty International is opposed to violence; it always tries to use other ways of getting its message across. Jot down all the non-violent ways you can think of which would draw the world's attention to the plight of a prisoner of conscience.
  - Watch out for mention of Amnesty International in the newspapers and on the television news.

THE PEN IS MIGHTIER THAN THE SWORD

> Amnesty International have discovered that letters written by ordinary people can bring hope and freedom to people who are being oppressed.
>
> Many professional playwrights, poets and novelists also take up the pen to draw the world's attention to situations where human rights are being abused. Vaclav Havel, a Czech playwright, was himself imprisoned a number of times for speaking out against the oppressive regime in his country but after a peaceful revolution in 1989, Vaclav Havel was made President. Rock stars such as Sting, Peter Gabriel and Sinead O'Connor have tried to draw attention to abuses of human rights through the lyrics of their songs.

5 Find out about these plays and playwrights:

Tom Stoppard — *Professional Foul* and *Every Good Boy Deserves Favour*

Ariel Dorfman *Death and the Maiden*

Dario Fo *Accidental Death of an Anarchist*

Also look up:

Athol Fugard, Wole Soyinka, Hanif Kureishi and Vaclav Havel

6 You don't have to be famous to draw attention to what you feel about violations of human rights. In 1973 the military in Chile seized power from President Allende – the first socialist to have been elected in that country. 15,000 Allende supporters were killed and another 30,000 detained. The extract below was written by an 11 year old boy in London who imagined what it would have been like in Chile at that time.

> Pedro' s Last Day of Freedom
>
> My name is Pedro Spangolee, and I am fifteen. And I am in a Chilean jail. I have been in jail for two years, I have not seen my family for such a long time, I am beginning to forget what they look like. It'll be so bad, I don't even know if they are dead or alive. I can just remember my last day of freedom. I got up feeling hungry. As usual, my little brother Manuel was already awake. There was no food so I went out to get some. Some of the people were in the market, or what was left of it. There was going to be a demonstration. A man walked up to me, he must have been the leader of the demonstration. The soldiers must have been watching the market. There was a scuffle and a scream and before I could run, the soldier had handcuffed me and dragged me into the back of the van. One of the soldiers punched me in the kidney. I was taken to the interrogation room. The soldier in the room pushed me into the chair and tied my hands behind the chair. Then he beat me and made me confess to the charges of which I had not committed. So they put me in jail. So that ends my story and I just hope that one day I will be free.
>
> *David Burman, 11*

Look back at the list of human rights abuses on p. 53. Choose one of the situations to work on in the exercises below:

- Write a number of monologues like the one by David Burman above which describe how people have been affected by the situation you have chosen.

- Imagine these 'statements' are to be used by Amnesty International in an appeal on television. Work in small groups and decide how you would read them out.
- What else would be said and done to make such an appeal effective?

PICTURES WITH A PURPOSE

Although cartoon drawings sometimes are thought of as being rather inferior to 'proper art' their simplicity can give an immediate powerful message. Some artists use cartoons to capture the 'essence' of their ideas. Others have turned the form into a weapon against the establishment; some were persecuted for doing so (Georg Grosz and Otto Dix were famous German cartoonists who had to flee from Hitler). Ralph Steadman, one of Britain's leading cartoonists, writes: '*A cartoon's purpose is not just to be funny. It is a sad fact, but oppression, deceit, and injustice are the mothers of satire, the cartoonist's best weapon.*'

7 To satirise something is to criticise it by making it look ridiculous. What do you think Ralph Steadman means when he says 'oppression, deceit, and injustice are the mothers of satire'?

- Look at these cartoons. What comment are they making on the news items that inspired them?
- Make a collection of cartoons which comment on current news events and display them with the headlines of the stories they are commenting on.

War between Nigeria and Biafra 1970 – 'Did we win, mama?'

Famine in Somalia 1992 – Colin Wheeler's 'Nude Photos fail to interest world'

British firms accused of selling arms to Saddam Hussein before the Gulf War in 1990 – Peter Brooks 'Made in Britain'

8 Some satirists use actual photographs to make fun of important or famous people by pasting in speech balloons. Private Eye magazine, a famous satirical paper which frequently gets into trouble for the way it criticises people, uses this technique for its front cover.

- Collect some newspaper pictures which show politicians or 'important' people appearing to say something.
- Display the pictures so that the whole class can consider what speech bubbles might fit the various pictures.
- The aim of this exercise isn't just to be rude. Discuss which ideas work as satire; that is, which ones make a critical comment as well as being laughable.

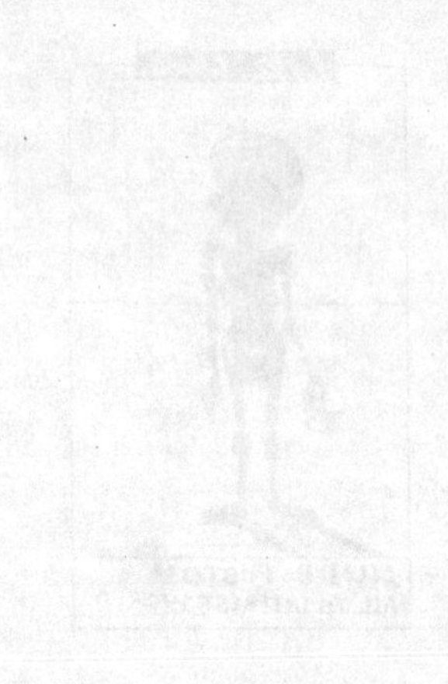